This book comes to you as a gift from Scottish Book Trust, as part of our Book Week Scotland celebrations. Up to 150,000 of these books will be given away all over Scotland.

Book Week Scotland takes place from 21-27 November 2016 and is Scotland's national celebration of books and reading. Throughout the week, libraries, schools, museums, arts venues and workplaces will host a packed programme of events, encouraging people of all ages to celebrate the pleasure of books and reading. Visit bookweekscotland.com for full listings of Book Week Scotland events, reading inspiration, book lists, podcasts, author interviews, and much more.

Scottish Book Trust believes that books and reading have the power to change lives. As a national charity, we inspire and support the people of Scotland to read and write for pleasure.

We give free books to every child in Scotland to ensure families of all backgrounds can share the joy of books at home. We work with teachers to inspire children to develop a lifelong love of reading with our innovative classroom resources, book awards and touring authors programme. We support the country's dynamic writing talent with skills development and mentoring, and fund all sorts of author events with the public, including schools, libraries, hospitals, festivals and reading/writing groups. We celebrate reading in all its forms and promote Scottish writing to people worldwide.

scottishbooktrust.com

Secrets and Confessions

scottishbooktrust.com

First published 2016 by Scottish Book Trust, Sandeman House,
Trunk's Close, 55 High Street, Edinburgh EH1 1SR

scottishbooktrust.com

A CIP catalogue record for this book is available from
the British Library

Typeset by 3btype.com

Printed and bound by CPI Group (UK) Ltd, Croydon, CR0 4YY

Scottish Book Trust makes every effort to ensure that the
paper used in this book has been legally sourced from
well-managed and certified forests.

Cover photograph © Adrian Searle; design by Freight Design

This is a free book, designed to be read alone or in groups, enjoyed,
shared and passed on to friends. This book is gifted to you by
Scottish Book Trust for Book Week Scotland 2016.

ePub and Kindle editions of this book are available from
scottishbooktrust.com/secretsandconfessions.

COMHAIRLE NAN
LEABHRAICHEAN
THE GAELIC BOOKS COUNCIL

Contents

* Stories marked with * are by published authors.

Bad Behaviourism

Lisa McInerney

I am not academically gifted. I am academically jammy, which is fair compensation. I lucked out with wonderful teachers in secondary school, who shouted at me *as Gaeilge* until I was able to shout back, or stayed after hours to give extra lessons in Maths and French. There were Saturday study sessions too, during which I would feverishly write things unconnected to my schoolwork: screenplays about teenaged thieves, short stories about substance abuse (I was reading a lot of Melvin Burgess at the time). Nevertheless, my teachers' pains led to my scraping together enough points in my Leaving Certificate to secure a place at University College Cork studying Arts. Participants took four subjects in first year, of which we were to choose two for subsequent years. I decided on English, Geography, Sociology and Psychology.

Six weeks after I turned seventeen I moved the hundred miles south to attend UCC. I started out diligent about my coursework, comprehensive in my reading. Textbooks had an esoteric, foreboding scholarly depth, each one a little Necronomicon; I would bury my nose in the pages and inhale. Arriving early to lectures, I found others who, like me, were new to freedom, whose faces couldn't hide the many minute blisses of pristine adulthood. We clutched folders, tapped pens off our teeth, made eye contact, ventured witticisms. Outside the lecture halls of the Boole Basement I found other young men and women who would walk with me to buy paper-cup coffees and take flyers for cheap club nights and stand in queues at the university bank for grant advances. The air throbbed with all manner of excitements: longing, bass, traffic, dashing steps.

But I made time to be alone, to pick my way around Cork City. I learned the bus routes and the landmarks – the red brick in Shanakiel, Father Mathew's statue, Sir Henry's, Fitzgerald Park. I learned the split courses of the Lee and the layout of the English Market, which clubs played which musical genres, and, as I was still too young to legally drink, the names of relevant bouncers and barmen. I got a feel for the place. I fell in love with the place. I fell in love with the place and out of love with my studies.

It is not necessarily conducive to academic learning to expand your brain; in fact, in the wrong head (mine) the two are mutually exclusive. The wider my sky got, the stronger my voice became, the surer my feet fell … the less captivating academia seemed. I decided which two of my four subjects I would drop: Sociology and Psychology, which I found interesting as a source of ideas for post-club conversation, but otherwise kind of pointless (being seventeen, I assumed I already knew everything about life, love and social mores). English and Geography felt more vital, so when I had to work I worked on them. And over Psychology and Sociology I chose the physiology of Cork City.

The teeming Arts I student body couldn't fit in on-campus examination halls, so we were directed all over the city to sit our end-of-year exams: to the Neptune Stadium in Blackpool, the Silver Springs Hotel in Tivoli and other places. I didn't have the money to pay for the arranged buses. My mapping of the city came in handy; I could just walk. So it was on the day of my Psychology exam.

But it occurred to me, as I set out, that maybe I might

have paid a little more heed to the subjects I'd chosen to study. That maybe I was being a bit cavalier. That I didn't have the bus fare because university was an expensive pursuit. I resolved to work harder in second year and do UCC's various fees justice. Free of Sociology and Psychology, I would knuckle down. I would have both: the streets and my degree.

I reached the venue and sat with friends, waiting on the bell, going over notes.

'My biggest worry,' said one buddy, 'is the question on cognitive psychology.'

'Cognitive,' I said. 'Cognitive is what again?'

'What d'you mean, is what again? It's a module. The middle one.'

'There's a module on cognitive psychology?'

My friend dug out a timetable and jabbed at it.

'How,' he cried, 'could you miss an entire module?'

But how could I not, in my urban rambles and diggings and viewings? In my delight at being grown and untethered I had managed to overlook the entire middle section of my Psychology course (ironically the section that deals with attention and memory). And now I had ten minutes to prep for regurgitation of the behemoth of human knowledge that is the study of the processes of the mind.

Cognitive psychology also deals with problem solving and creativity.

These I understood well enough after years of academic jamminess. Frantically, I theorised that I could pass Psychology if I was sufficiently glib on the page; I'd spent all those hours at Saturday study writing fiction; this was just another application. Without a way around it I battled through it, as a desperate explorer machetes her way through the rainforest. I sat in that exam hall and vomited one thousand words of bombastic gobbledygook. I camouflaged my ignorance with common sense made to seem erudite by assuredly applied palaver.

I passed that exam, and so the module, and so the whole first year of college. I passed on pretence and brass neck, by the seat of my pants. I am still not entirely sure what I might learn by studying cognitive psychology, but I know what I learned by not studying it: how to find myself in the city – and how to write my way out of anything.

The Unsung Hero

Norma Austin Hart

My grandpa was a quiet man. He was a soldier. He had a box of medals from the First World War. When my dad was a wee boy, he'd try to box with my grandpa. 'Faither, tell me aboot the war, tell me aboot the fightin.' Grandpa would swat Dad away like a wee midgie then trudge around the garden and lop the heads off his roses. My dad told me that Grandpa would walk for miles in the fields behind the house, hands clasped at his back.

My granny and grandpa lived three doors up from us. I thought their house was my house too. I knew where my granny kept everything. She had a big jeely pan under the sink to make jam and soak the tripe in milk. She would birl the big, white, stretchy bands of cow's stomach along her arms as I gasped, eyes wide. She kept six teeny tiny silver spoons in a fancy box in her cupboard beside her bed. They were mine she said, if I was good.

My grandpa taught me when to chap at dominoes. 'Hiv patience bairn.' He showed me how to win at draughts. 'Surprise!' He murmured when my granny shouted at the wrestlers on the telly, 'She thinks they can hear her.' He let me fill in his pools coupon. 'Ye can have half if we win.' And he taught me sign language because he was deaf. Not hard of hearing. Completely totally deaf. My granny had to stamp her foot in the kitchen to get him to come for his tea.

My grandpa was a stretcher-bearer with the Kosbies in the war. Uncle Jim said he must've seen some awful bloody sights. 'Unsung heroes,' he said. They didn't have guns, they didn't fight. They had to go out into the no-man's-land to find the dead and dying. On 12 October 1917 my grandpa was carrying an injured man back to the trench. This was during the first battle of Passchendaele. 'There wisnae much passion,' Uncle Jim said. A mortar exploded about twenty yards away from them. Uncle Jim said Grandpa didn't notice much at the time. He was too busy getting himself, the other stretcher-bearer and the injured man through the mire and mud. It was the last sound he heard clearly.

Uncle George said after Grandpa came home he didn't speak much. Granny could speak for both of them, Uncle Jim said. Maybe he didn't like the sound of his own voice inside his head. Grandpa grew used to silence. He whispered his prayers with his papery hands folded like a kirk roof and his eyes closed.

When I came along he'd been deaf nearly forty years. He'd sit for hours looking at the fire. I'd watch him, wondering what was going through his mind. So I kept him busy. He was my patient when I was the nurse and let me take his temperature with a pencil, wipe his brow with a tea towel. He was my pupil, my audience. He did his sums and clapped when I bowed. He nodded at my picture-book stories and chuckled at my faulty signing.

Then I went to school. The children's rules in the playground were harsh. The teachers watched us from the staffroom. Smelly, fat, stupid children were targeted first. Outside school, an adult who couldn't tell you off was a novelty, a rare treat. I sniggered up my cardi sleeve when the big kids shouted at Mongo Jean and Cripple Jock when they were at the caff. I hid behind the wall when my dad came to shoo us away.

Me and Margaret were the babies of the gang. Her big sister Pamela was first with any mischief. 'It was in

Baghdad when ma mammy met ma dad…' we sang,
snorting like wee piggies. One summer afternoon I was
in the park with Margaret. We sat on the grass, making
long garlands of daisy chains. In the distance I heard,
'There's auld deefie Austin!' My heart hurt inside my
chest. I stared down at my daisies, but Pamela spied me
over the heads of the other children.

'Hi, wee yin! Bet yer grandpa isnae deef at a!'

'Aye he is!'

'Prove it.' Arms folded like her mother. 'Gan richt up
tae him an shout deefie ahin his back.'

All the eyes of the gang turned to me. I wish I could say
I threw down my daisy chain, stamped my foot, ran away.
I wish I could say I even hesitated. With a hop, a skip
and another skip I ran up behind my beloved grandpa as
he trudged along and yelled 'deeeeeefie' with all my
childish heart.

My dad was there out of nowhere. He scooped me up
and carried me under his arm to the shop where he sat
me on the back step and hunkered down in front of me.
'Please dinnae tell him,' I sobbed.

'Ah dinnae need tae.' He held my hands. 'Ah dinnae
know how he knows an it disnae really matter.' He passed
me his hanky. 'Ah did the same when ah wis a wean an he
forgave me too.' I calmed down in the cool shade of the
canopy, the daisies limp round my neck, breathing in the
clean smell of my dad's white shop coat.

'But lassie' – his index finger under my chin – 'when he
comes in, tell him you're sorry.' He stood up and circled
his fist over his heart. 'Show him you mean it. You know
whit tae dae.' I blew my nose and practised my sign for
sorry until my granny turned the lights off and I heard
my grandpa open the shop door.

Accident

Mhairi Mackay

I really didn't mean to hit him with the car. That's the truth. Even though everyone knew I hated him, it was a genuine accident. Even if I had looked, I probably wouldn't have seen him, but it was undeniably my fault that he was dead.

I remember reading while I was pregnant about emotions, and how I would become eloquently compassionate towards all living things, like the mother fox who ushers an orphaned bear cub to her breast with her other tiny foxlets.

That wasn't me. I felt like a soldier from the trenches returning home devastated. I had suffered for a week then I was drugged, slashed open then kicked home with a screaming potato, a box of painkillers and a welcome pack of warnings that still lay in a suitcase of mould-smelling clothes at the bottom of the stairs.

I was no nurturer. I wasn't one of those wonderful mothers who could knit a reusable nappy whilst breastfeeding, simultaneously singing word-perfect rhymes and accommodating nuisance in-laws. I was possibly a bleach drinker or a traffic dancer, someone who might be inspired.

I wasn't meant to be outside, but I hadn't smelled fresh air since they deposited me at the front door with the potato. When the potato slept, I could move around and pretend I was me again. I missed my long drives with my crisps and juice and songs. Maybe that's why I started the car. I wanted to hear the engine and smell the petrolly dusty smells. A small manoeuvre would be enough. Just close my eyes and feel the pedals.

It was barely an accident. Barely a hit. Nobody would believe that though. I wasn't credible anymore. I had lost my marbles to the mothering disease, and I should have been hiding in my hole with my boobs out and my brain in the sink.

I should have felt sorry, but I didn't. I really hated him. I hated the way he used to watch me from his window when I came home from work. He would sneer at me from the garden, and I would always be the first one to break the stare because he made me so uncomfortable. He relished in it. He was a bully and he treated everyone with the same chauvinistic disrespect.

He would often stand at his door, shouting to his woman to let him in or to get his dinner ready. She would let him treat her with such abusive disrespect, and she didn't even bother to hide the marks he left on her. It was disgusting. Of all the neighbours to have, he was the most despicable, the most twisted and the most sinister, yet people failed to see it. They saw the gentleman, the fancy attire, the schmoozer.

I saw him late one evening using my African violets as a toilet. He knew I could see him, but he swanned off knowing that he had such luscious power. If I had called the police they would have laughed and accused me of time-wasting.

I sat on the toilet seat for a long time, looking at his lifeless body in the bath. I was in fiery pain from getting him there, and I was truly exhausted. My eyes were fixed through him, and my futile mind was battling the vapour, trying to decide what to do.

The police really would have been useless. My neighbours would have found out and run me out of town because of their admiration of him. My family would have lectured. I would have lost my licence for driving in my condition and gone to jail for murdering without valid insurance.

I had two weeks before my husband came home. I had two days before the midwife called round again. I maybe had two minutes before the potato needed me. I had to make sure I did a clean job and disposed of this disaster. I could deal with this. I just needed to think.

I waited until the next round of feeding, burping, vomiting, nappying, screaming and drowsiness had rolled around before I returned to the bathroom with the knives, gloves, bags, nose plug, bleach, goggles and music.

It was much easier than I thought. My dad's knife-sharpening demonstrations certainly made the bones easy to deal with. I decided to keep my eyes open. I didn't have any vocabulary left for mistakes. I told myself that this revenge was delicious. I wasn't a convincing liar, but it was good enough.

I had to stash the parts in the freezer in the garage. I needed to keep the stench to a minimum while I took care of the disposal. I could have used the bin, but it was risky. I wasn't allowed to move the bin yet and anyone could lift the lid and smell the death. I also worried about haunting, and a proper disposal might help towards a peaceful afterlife.

The head was first to go. It was important. It had the sneering looks, the memories and the identity. I managed to ram it into the bottom of the pram and I got as far as the path to the woods before I knelt on my squashy mat with my trowel.

There were seven burials altogether. I managed it all in a week. He was dispersed around his town in beautiful places, and I'm sure that if he could put aside the accidental murder, I think he would have been pleased with the arrangements.

Then the day came when she arrived at the door, forlorn and worried. I spied her from the landing window and watched. Eventually she gave up. I knew my silence was much better than my terrible lying.

As she left, I felt a sudden urge to ease her pain, but stopped myself like an ugly brake. I fondled the little red velvet collar in my pocket, the one with the little bell, the bell that never jingled loudly enough the day I reversed over him.

Untitled

David

Before I came to rehab I didn't understand what was
wrong with me. Drugs took their toll on me. I was a filthy,
underweight drug addict with hepatitis C. I was up at
court constantly reading not guilty when I was physically
and mentally unhealthy. I had no one in my life – my
family left me. But me being an addict, I blamed it on
them. When I came to rehab I found out that I was the
problem, not the drugs. I didnae want tae hear it. I was
screaming a need for earplugs: just give me ma meth –
am dying of a violent death. But then one day the penny
dropped – am aff ma detox. I've learned some recovery
tools and they're not aff a cereal box. The sky's the limit
not the treetops. One day at a time. It's so simple, not
easy, but hey it's mine.

The Summer of Jimi Hendrix

Mark Wightman

It was Singapore, 1972. The school holidays seemed to last forever that summer, and the highlight was the day I found Jimi Hendrix.

Carp bite best when the sun is still low and the water is cool. My brother and I had stopped on the way to the fishing pond and bought newly baked bread from the Chinese bakery on Lim Chu Kang Road. We pulled big soft chunks of the bread and sprinkled it with aniseed water and put half the bread onto the hooks and ate the other half. We could see the fish circling, the rings of water giving them away as they kissed the surface. It was a bit too easy. The fish liked the aniseed bread too much, and we liked catching them too much, so you could say it wasn't really fair. But we loved doing it anyway. Later, when the sun was up and the dragonflies had started to dance, the fish would head down deep, into the cooler water. We tried more exotic fare in our attempts to entice them: mashed-up boiled tapioca, corn, cubes of cheese, even worms, but we knew there was really nothing for it but to wait it out until the sun dropped again.

We sat around for a while making up stories, trying to outdo each other with the tallest tale, which we would always swear was absolutely true, till we got bored. Leaving my fishing rod under the eye of a curious kingfisher, I went scavenging and came across a rusty old landing net, half-hidden by reeds at the edge of the pond. It was stuck fast, and it took a few good pulls to get it out, but it was worth the effort, because tangled up in the net was a terrapin as big as a generous-sized dinner plate. We asked Mr Lim, the owner of the pond, if he had a box. Neither my brother nor I were sure about the rules for taking terrapins on public transport so we covered him with a towel and hoped he wouldn't make a noise and distract the bus driver. He never made a sound, as far as I remember.

When we got him home, I constructed a pen in the corner of the garden from bits of discarded wood and chicken wire. By this time, I had decided on his name. I rummaged around till I found a tin of red paint in amongst the gardening tools, and using an old, fat calligraphy brush made from bamboo and pig hair, bristles stiff with dirt and age, I painted his name on his back, painstakingly following the partitions on his shell to keep the lettering neat. Diet was a bit of an issue to begin with – he was a fussy eater. It seemed terrapins didn't care much for hamburger, or cheese, or bread, or fried rice, or dried salted plums. At least this one didn't. After a bit of experimenting, I discovered terrapins were, on the other hand, rather partial to lettuce, mango, papaya, jackfruit and more lettuce.

Once he had settled in to his new home, I rigged up a harness from an old dog lead so I could let him out of his compound. I tied one end of a piece of washing line to the harness and the other end to a pole and lifted him out so he could roam loose around the garden. When he realised he had a modicum of freedom he clambered up onto the tips of his gnarled legs, like a boat raising itself up onto hydrofoils, and off he charged. People that had only seen tortoises crawling around had trouble believing how quickly a terrapin could move. He gave the dog a fair run for her money as she ran alongside, barking at this odd-looking intruder with the custom paint job. We had a great summer, Jimi Hendrix and me. He had real character, and you couldn't say that about too many terrapins.

It ended as suddenly as it had begun, later on that year. I came out to his pen one morning with a bowl of lettuce to find him completely lifeless. No amount of coaxing and no amount of tears induced him to stir. My father told me sometimes these things are just meant to be, and my mother told me how smart he had looked with his red name and she was sure he'd been very happy during his time with us. I found an old metal tin and placed Jimi inside, and taped the box up so the ants couldn't get in. I took him to an overgrown piece of scrubland, where he wouldn't be disturbed, and buried him.

I wish I had known more about terrapins then. I wish I had known how to feed him properly, and I wish I had known he needed shade from the height of the sun and access to water, to keep him cool. I suppose, looking back, I wish I had just left him where I had found him on that day back at the start of the holidays. But most of all, I wish I had known that, even in the tropics, where the temperature rarely dropped below 28°C, some species of terrapins still hibernate, and when they hibernate they appear exactly as though they are dead.

Confessions of a Palaeontologist

Steve Brusatte

I'm a palaeontologist – a scientist who digs up dinosaurs for a living. One of the perks of the job is that people always seem to be interested in what I'm finding. Especially the press. Journalists sniff out new dinosaurs like those Italian pigs sniff out truffles. I've been blessed a few times now to wake up in the morning and see my beaming mug in *The Guardian* or *The Times* or some dastardly tabloid, next to some hyperbolic headline about some new dinosaur that I uncovered in some corner of the globe.

But here's my dirty little secret: I don't particularly like fieldwork, and I'm not particularly good at it.

Don't get me wrong, I love travelling the world, working with all kinds of amazing scientists, venturing into the badlands and emerging with 100-million-year-old bones of spectacular creatures that no human has ever seen before.

It's just not my favorite part of the job. I would much rather be sitting by my computer writing up a description of a new dinosaur, or working on a book, or giving a lecture, or even teaching. That's a sacrilegious thing for a paleontologist to say, as we're supposed to be a special breed of rugged explorers.

But rugged I am most certainly not. I can camp and cook over the campfire and hack dinosaur bones out of the ground and all of that stuff, but I'm pretty mediocre at it. And that all comes down to a twist of family history that left me in the sad position that I'm in today.

There are many things that boys usually learn from their fathers – what sports teams to love and hate, what vocabulary to use when you stub your toe, how to treat girls and how to use your hands. To hunt, to fish, to build things. But my father can't build anything, and thus neither can I.

It's not his fault. He was never taught.

But his father could build things. His pops, my grandfather, Louis, was a strong, vivacious, fast-talking Italian-American who raised his brood of four girls and my father in the Chicago suburbs in the 1950s. His garage was full of tools, his workbench a thing to behold. Extended family from far and wide would ask him to fix this or install that, and he would oblige, especially if you gave him a few beers or some slices of watermelon.

Making things was also his job. He forged steel at the US steelworks in Joliet, Illinois, once one of the biggest mills in the US. It was hot, nasty, muscle-shredding work. But Louis was a legend – the short little guy was one of the hardest workers around.

But then one day everything changed.

Louis was going about his work, just another day on the job, a few more hours to go and then his wife and kids would be waiting for him, dinner on the table. Far above him, something slipped and then came crashing down – thud. It was a bale of wire, weighing more than 1,000 pounds. And it fell right on Louis' hip.

It was a miracle that he didn't die. He almost lost one of his legs to a blood clot, but he pulled through. But he was permanently deformed, a once proud man reduced to a cripple. He couldn't cook steel anymore, so the mill put him to work in maintenance. For a while he was still able to build things, but after a few years that became too difficult. So they made him into a custodian. A janitor. He unclogged toilets and cleaned up spills.

That was around the time my father was born. When my dad was growing up, his father's tools gathered dust, his workbench sat silent, like a museum exhibit to the man who once was. There was no father-son bonding over hammers and saws and chisels. And when Louis died when my father was a teenager, an uncle came over and swept the tools into his truck, drove off and that was that.

My father became a lawyer, a lover of books, somebody whose idea of hell is mowing the grass on Sunday or trimming hedges or trying to sort the basement when the sump pump stops working. We had a toolbox at home when I was growing up, but it was more for decoration, and I never learned much beyond the basics of how to hammer a nail.

As a palaeontologist I build family trees of ancient organisms. Genealogies that show how the dinosaurs were related to each other, which we need in order to study their evolution. But it's my own family tree that explains how I got to where I am today: a palaeontologist who isn't so good at digging up dinosaurs.

When All You Need is a Fan Heater

Claire Brunton

I felt my left finger twitch and I dug my nails into the fleshy part of my lower back. It formed part of a ritual to create a memorable mark on my skin, remind me where I had placed my hand. That's when I have to really concentrate; clear my mind and focus. I guess it's similar to meditation, my kind of meditation. Time I can really zone out, let all the worries from the day sort themselves out into little compact boxes. Of course, it always seems easier sat in a room surrounded by people who by all intents and purposes are in need of my presence but not in need of me.

Tonight it was my leg's turn to feel the numbness. Initially it always feels comfortable, and I tell myself it's only for twenty minutes, but invariably it turns into half an hour. The minutes I count in my head intertwine with the music playing in the background. I start again. One elephant, two elephants, three… It's how to count seconds accurately, I am told. No one tells you about the pace though. I wonder what the artists would think if I told them that tonight I'd replaced the elephants for the Pinball song from *Sesame Street*.

Sometimes I'll abandon the chanting of numbers and instead I'll listen to the sounds being created around me: persistent scratches of charcoal; the chink of paintbrushes against glass as water is stirred; frogs in throats clearing and the hum of a fan heater.

There are smells too that accompany the sounds,

sometimes metallic, powdery dust, a hint of oil (petroleum not olive) and hairspray. It curls around the back of my throat, iritates, but usually I manage to refrain from coughing until I have reached the end of the pose.

I smile to myself as I know my workmates would be shocked to know how I spend some of my evenings. By way of polite chit-chat and the invariable question 'So what do you have on tonight?' I skirt around the truth of my exact extra-curricular activity and simply say, 'Not much.'

Tonight there is no hairspray, just the ingrained scent of paint that has been layered over the years onto the floor and easels. A fresh breeze meanders in pleasant whorls around the room. It's now summer and I have no need for the fan heater. The room is airy, but still a comfortable temperature and I can hear the bleating of nearby sheep in a field as the door has been left ajar. I chat with the artists, people who have become more than just familiar faces. It is ironic that I build up stories of their lives, and they also learn about me, yet while I catch a glimpse of who they are, they always see more of me.

In between poses I will wander between easels and see how others perceive me or have adapted me to their own image. It's one of my favourite parts of the evening, I'll recognise my thigh or breast whether roughly sketched in charcoal or in subtle splashes of colour. A line is enough to capture a pose, while each artist's style comes alive on the paper.

It's not always accurate but what a privilege to view myself through others' eyes and see the change in my body over the years. It can be a great eye-opener – not least by the noticeable increase around the midriff. The funny thing is, you would never catch me in a bikini as I'm too self-conscious of the constricted lumpy bits, but place me in a room where creativity is desperate to escape, I too escape and without care drop my robe.

So I keep this secret from my place of work and can only imagine the reaction in the middle of a discussion about what happened in last night's *Eastenders*, if my input was, 'Well at least you weren't standing with your arse against a cold mirror, while your left leg went to sleep.'

Sugar Frosties

Frances Ainslie

Breakfast time, and my dad, Mick, sat at the table crunching his Frosties and slurping milk. He marked a line on the box. The Frosties were his and never shared with anyone. We had porridge.

'Pleeease can I go?' I leaned in between him and his spoon.

'Whit in hell's name are ye wantin tae go there fur?' he said.

Tony the Tiger grinned at me from the box, his red kerchief tied at a cute angle. 'They're grrreat!' said Tony. Mick wasn't grinning. He wasn't bouncy like Tony either. I looked at Mum. She raised a perfectly tweezered eyebrow.

'But all the girls in my class go,' I whined. Mick hated whining.

'Sho?' he slurred, his mouth bulging with Frosties.

'Fiona Anderson goes.' I folded my arms, the way my nana did when she was making a point.

'Good fur bloody her!'

'They made pompoms last week.'

Mum shuffled in her chair and hid behind the *Dundee Courier*.

'Bloody pompoms! What feckin use are they?' I ducked a spray of Frosties pulp as it hit the tangerine zig-zag wallpaper.

'She only wants to join the Girls' Brigade, Mick,' said Mum sleepily, not lifting her eyes from the newspaper. The only sound was the bar on the electric fire buzzing away like a wasp.

'Holy Wullies the bloody lot o them.' He slammed the door on his way out.

Mum shook her head and tutted. I stuck out my bottom lip and squeezed my eyes shut till I heard the rattle of padlocks and the rusty iron door scrape open at the back of the house. That would be him under a car bonnet until tea time.

'I know,' Mum crooned. 'We'll just keep workin on him … and you, madam, you need tae learn when tae hud yer tongue.'

Tony the Tiger smirked at me from the front of the big cardboard box. I poked his eye with my fork. If Mick didn't let me go, I'd gob into his Frosties packet and run away – then he'd be sorry. Fiona Anderson was lucky – she had a nice dad, a big brother and a piano that she never even played.

Mum switched on the wireless and started doing the twist.

'Next Thursday is Halloween. They're dookin for apples at the Girls' Brigade,' I said.

'That's nice, dear. Apples are good for yer teeth. When I was a wee girl, we had scones on strings, slathered in treacle.' She lit a fag. She always had one after Mick went out. I kicked the leg of his chair till there was a bash in the toe of my sandal. She bent low mid twist, the fag dangling from her lips, and scudded my legs hard. She then took a long draw and blew the smoke at the ceiling where it spiralled up to settle in the yellow corners of the room. The place always smelled of damp, and the wallpaper curled loose at the seams. Mick pasted down the edges every so often. Days later, it just sprang loose again. The scullery ceiling was flecked with mildew, spiders ran wild everywhere and we had a mouse.

The Andersons didn't have one of them!

I cleared the breakfast stuff from the table and rattled cups in the scullery sink before heading back to the living room.

'Fiona said you get badges for knittin and bible readin at the Girls' Brigade,' I said. Mum sighed and shook her head. 'Why can't I go?'

'We'll see. He'll be in soon enough. Manky wi oil and happy as Larry.' She tightened the ribbon on my pigtail. 'And we're havin sausage an onion casserole for tea.' She winked.

Later, the back door blew open, and I heard Mick at the sink rubbing his hands with Swarfega green frogspawny stuff that stank. The grey lather stretched to his elbows. I hovered by the kitchen door and watched his back. He turned around, grinned and waved his smelly hands in my face before he eased himself out of his overalls and groaned into the chair by the fire.

'It's bloody cauld in yon garage,' he said, as he eyed the latest wallpaper seam to become unstuck. Mum switched on the TV for *Doctor Who*. She'd brushed her hair and put on a coat of red lipstick.

'I'm just away ben the scullery tae check oan the sausage casserole,' she said, brushing the dark hairs on his forearm as she passed his chair.

I sat on the fireside rug at his feet, my back leaning into his legs. Every so often he'd nudge me with his knee. When the Cybermen came on, I'd always squeal and hide behind a cushion, but I stayed quiet through the whole episode. Mum brought him a mug of tea and a digestive biscuit. He wiggled his feet in front of the fire.

'So, lady, what's wi this Girl Scout nonsense?' he said.

'It's the Girls' Brigade.'

'It'll mean goin tae the Kirk I suppose?' He shook his head as if the prospect was hopeless. Mick didn't believe in God, or Jesus even. 'It'll no work, if yer mither's tae get up early oan a Sunday mornin.' I stared at the TV and nibbled the soft skin at the side of my nails. 'Plus, how were ye plannin tae get there, eh?'

'Fiona Anderson's dad said he'd give me a lift.' I sniffed. 'He's got a nice blue car.'

He thought about this as he rubbed the soles of his socks together, sending up wee puffs of steam. In the scullery onions sizzled and Mum whistled along to the *Doctor Who* theme tune.

'Maybe me an him could dae week aboot. How does that sound?'

I couldn't answer him – all I could think of was how I'd manage to remove the gob from his Frosties packet.

Crashing

Sandra Kohls

It was kind of you to let me know,
So sad to hear the news.
I'll send some flowers and a card, of course
It won't be me who rocks upon the bed
with gasping breath.
It's been a lifetime, after all,
too long to be concerned
with a life from so long ago.

An accident you said, his car.
He always drove too fast.
A shock, he was too young to go.
So sorry that I won't be there
to mourn. It's truly not because
I couldn't bear the pain.
It's just that it's so far to come
for a life from so long ago.

It's really of no consequence
that I won't gaze upon the grave.
It's not that he would even know,
and no one else will care.
And anyway, what right have I
to steal a share of grief
from others with more claim than me
to a life from so long ago.

I'll pour a drop upon the floor,
play tributes, 'Back in Black',
and light a candle in his name.
Try and blunt the knife which slices
and serrates my younger soul,
the one he used to know so well,
because it's not as if I could miss him
a love from so long ago.

Feumaidh mi Aideachadh . . .
I Have to Confess . . .

Alison Lang

Gun do Ghoogle mi d' ainm.

Barrachd air aon turas. Iomadh turas, leis an fhìrinn innse.

Is nach do lorg mi mòran a bha gu feum sam bith.

Seann stuth, a' chuid as motha dheth, a' dol air ais deich bliadhna. Còrr is deich bliadhna. Còig bliadhna deug, is dòcha, nuair a bha sinn fhathast còmhla.

Ach cha bhithinn air a dhèanamh mura robh thusa air am post-d ud a chur thugam. Cha bhithinn, air m' onar. Nach b' e siud an t-aonta a bha eadarainn? A h-uile ceangal a bhriseadh, cuimhn' agad?

Feumaidh gun do rinn thusa an aon rud ormsa. Gam Ghoogleadh, no cha bhiodh tu air an teachdaireachd a chur dhan t-seòladh-obrach agam. Sin mise, nam shuidhe san oifis, pàipearan suas gu m' achlais, a' feuchainn ris na duilleagan a chur ann an òrdugh agus an tìde a' ruith orm, agus thàinig Ceitidh a-steach le cupan cofaidh dhomh. 'Gabh air do shocair,' thuirt i. 'Cha tig crìoch air an t-saoghal mura tèid iad a-mach a-nochd.' 'S i a bha air a socair. Sèimh, ciùin, cha robh dad sam bith ga cur suas no sìos.

Ceart, ma-tà. Còig mionaidean. Cupan cofaidh, agus sùil air a' phost-d. Agus bha d' ainm ann. Às dèidh deich bliadhna.

'Tha mi air a bhith a' sgioblachadh aig an taigh,' thuirt

thu, 'agus fhuair mi lorg air leabhraichean is rudan eile a bh' agad. Eil thu gan iarraidh air ais?'

Fhathast san aon flat? Dìreach air an stuth agam a lorg an-dràsta? Bha mi amharasach. Cha b' e siud an sgeul gu lèir, bha mi cinnteach às. Ach cha robh mi a' dol a dh'fhaighneachd.

Fhreagair mi sa mhionaid. 'Cuir gu bùth-chathrannais e. Rinn mi a' chùis às aonais fad deich bliadhna is chan eil mi ga iarraidh a-nis. Agus na cuir post-d eile thugam. Mar sin leat.'

Air ais gu na pàipearan. Bha Ceitidh ceart; ghabhadh a dhèanamh. A-mach sa phost agus b' urrainn dhomh anail a ghabhail a-rithist.

Ach cha b' urrainn dhomh. Bha mi air an conaltradh a dhùnadh sìos ach bha ceistean agam. Carson? Carson an-diugh? Dè bha a' dol nad bheatha? Dh'innis mi dhomh fhìn nach robh mi airson faighinn a-mach, nach robh fios agam agus nach robh mi ag iarraidh fios. Ach bha, agus fad na slighe dhachaigh bha na ceistean ag obair orm agus mo mhacmeanmna a' cruthachadh sgeulachdan. Rudan uabhasach a dh'fhaodadh a bhith a' tachairt. Dè rinn thu?

Nuair a ràinig mi an taigh, feumaidh mi aideachadh, chuir mi air mo choimpiutair sa bhad. Cha do smaoinich mi air biadh no telebhisean no an nigheadaireachd no an sgioblachadh a bha a dhìth air a' flat.

Dh'fheuch mi Google. Cha robh mòran ann air nach robh mi eòlach mar-thà. Rudan mun sgioba agad ann am farpais spòrs, ach bha sin a' dol air ais bliadhnaichean, nuair a bha thu fhathast an ceann an trèanaidh leis na balaich ud. Nuair a bha sinn fhathast còmhla. Ach sna còig bliadhna mu dheireadh? Naidheachd ionadail mu fhear a fhuair bàs, agus facal bhuatsa mun chall, oir bha thu eòlach air tro d' obair.

Facail iomchaidh, ag ràdh cho duilich 's a bha a h-uile duine mu na dh'èirich dha.

Ach dè bha air èirigh dhutsa? Carson a bha thu air sgrìobhadh thugam? Carson a-nis?

Feumaidh mi aideachadh gun robh mi a' faireachdainn gòrach an uair sin. Mura robh mi air freagairt cho luath is cho cinnteach a chur thugad, bhiodh cothrom agam na ceistean seo a chur ort. Ach bha mi air an conaltradh a dhùnadh sìos.

Na cuir fios thugam! B' e siud a dh'aontaich sinn! Tha beatha ùr agam a-nis! Na bi a' briseadh a-steach mar seo! Sin na bha air a bhith a' ruith tro m' inntinn sna còig mionaidean ud san oifis. Nan sgrìobhainn air ais thugad a-nis le ceistean … uill, cha bhiodh coltas math air sin.

Dh'fheuch mi Google a-rithist? Ainm agus sloinneadh. Prìomh litrichean d' ainm agus sloinneadh. A h-ainm-se? Seadh, a' chiad ainm aice agus do shloinneadh-sa. Ach dè an t-ainm a bh' oirre mus do phòs i thu? Cha robh cuimhne agam.

Tha sin ceart, cha robh cuimhne agam. B' e sin an t-aonta a bh' againn. Dìochuimhneachadh, gluasad air adhart, beatha ùr. Bha mise air sin a dhèanamh.

Cha robh Twitter gu mòran feum nas motha, no Facebook. Dè eile a b' urrainn dhomh feuchainn – an clàr-bhòtaidh? An robh sin air-loidhne? Nach robh a h-uile rud air-loidhne sna làithean seo?

A h-uile rud ach thusa. Bha mi a' lorg fear gun lorg.

Ach bha seòladh post-d agam air do shon a-nis. B' urrainn dhomh teachdaireachd a chur, ag ràdh …

Ag ràdh dè? Ag ràdh gun robh mi duilich nach do dh'fhaighnich mi na bu tràithe ciamar a bha thu, dè bha dol agad, càite an robh thu ag obair, rudan modhail mar sin? Cha robh dòigh fo ghrian a bha mi a' dol a ràdh 'duilich' riutsa.

Bha i air d' fhàgail, nach robh? Ise. An tè leis an sloinneadh air nach robh cuimhne agam. Sin as adhbhar a bha thu a' 'sgioblachadh'. Uill, feumaidh mi aideachadh gun robh e na iongnadh dhomh gun robh an dàimh agaibh air mairsinn cho fada sin.

Chuir mi dheth mo choimpiutair. Ach cha do sguir na smuaintean. Na ceistean. Na cuimhneachan. An t-aithreachas? Cha robh aithreachas orm. *Je ne regrette rien*, mar a sheinneas na Frangaich.

Ach … ach … bha mi duilich. Duilich nach robh an sgeulachd gu lèir agam. Amharas, seadh. Suidheachaidhean nam mhacmeanmna, gun teagamh. Ach an fhìrinn ghlan, an sgeulachd bhrònach air fad, cha bhiodh sin agam a chaoidh.

An ath-latha rinn mi Google ort a-rithist. Agus an latha às dèidh sin. Agus a-rithist às dèidh seachdain. Neoni. Ach gus an cuireadh tu fios thugam a-rithist, cha robh càil eile a b' urrainn dhomh dèanamh.

* * *

That I Googled your name.

More than once. Many times, truth be told.

And that I didn't find much that was of any use at all.

Old stuff, most of it, going back ten years. More than ten years. Fifteen years, perhaps, when we were still together.

But I wouldn't have done it if you hadn't sent me that email. Honestly, I wouldn't. Wasn't that what we had agreed? To sever all links, remember?

You must have done the same to me. Googled me, or you wouldn't have sent the message to my work address. There I was, sitting in the office, up to my armpits in paperwork, trying to get the pages in order and with time running out, and Katie came in with a cup of coffee for me. 'Take it easy,' she said. 'The world won't end if they don't go out tonight.' She was a cool one. Calm, unruffled – nothing could fluster her.

Alright then. Five minutes. A cup of coffee and a peek at my email. And there was your name. After ten years.

'I've been tidying the house,' you said, 'and I found some books and other things of yours. Do you want them back?'

Still in the same flat? Only just found my stuff now? I was suspicious. That wasn't the whole story, I was certain of it. But I wasn't going to ask.

I responded immediately. 'Take it to a charity shop. I've managed without it for ten years, and I don't need it now. And don't email me again. Goodbye.'

Back to the paperwork. Katie was right; it was doable. All posted out and I could breathe again.

Except that I couldn't. I'd shut down the conversation, but I had questions. Why? Why today? What was going on in your life? I told myself that I didn't want to find out, that I didn't know and didn't want to know. But I did, and all the way home the questions were nagging at me, and my imagination was making up stories. Awful things that might be happening. What had you done?

When I got home, I have to confess, I switched on my computer instantly. I didn't think about food or television or the washing or tidying the flat, though it needed doing.

I tried Google. There wasn't much I didn't already know. Things about your sports team in competitions, but that was going back years, when you were still training those lads. When we were still together. But in the past five years? A local news story about a man who had died, and a comment from you, who had known him through work. Appropriate words, saying how sorry everyone was about what had happened to him.

But what had happened to you? Why were you writing to me? Why now?

I have to confess that I felt foolish then. If I hadn't answered so fast and with such certainty, I could have asked you these questions. But I had shut down the conversation.

Don't contact me! That was what we agreed! I've got a new life now! Don't break in like this! That's what was running through my mind during those five minutes in the office. If I wrote back now with questions... well, that wouldn't look so good.

I tried Google again. Name and surname. Your initials and surname. Her name? Yes, her first name and your surname. But what was her name before she married you? I couldn't remember.

That's right, I couldn't remember. That was the deal we made. Forget, move on, new life. I for one had done that.

Twitter wasn't much use either, and neither was Facebook. What else could I try – the electoral register? Was that online? Wasn't everything online these days?

Everything but you. I was hunting a man who left no trace.

But I had your email address now. I could send you a message, saying...

Saying what? Saying I was sorry not to have asked you earlier how you were, what you were doing, where you were working and other such pleasantries? There was no way I was going to say 'sorry' to you.

She had left you, hadn't she? Her. Her with the surname I couldn't remember. That's why you were 'tidying'. Well, I have to confess that I was surprised your relationship had lasted that long.

I switched off the computer. But that didn't stop the thoughts. The questions. The memories. The regrets? I didn't feel any regret. *Je ne regrette rien*, as the French folk are wont to sing.

But… but… I was sorry. Sorry that I didn't know the whole story. Suspicions, yes. Imagined scenarios, undoubtedly. But the truth, the whole sorry tale – I would probably never know that.

The next day I Googled you again. And the day after that. And again a week later. Nothing. But until you contacted me again, there was nothing else I could do.

My Secret Beach

Zoe Sutherland

My family and I have a secret beach,
Which is not far from our house.
I don't think many people know about it,
Because we usually have it to ourselves.

We often go there and have a picnic,
And collect wood to make a fire.
We cook sausages and then go paddling.

I enjoy spending time there.
It is so peaceful.

Pluggin It

Ailie Wallace

Ah shrieked as something sharp jagged intae ma finger. Ah'd no been peyin heed whaur Ah wis going, and Ah stumbled right intae some barbed wire, which had been stretched across the field. Nae doubt it had been laid by the farmer tae stop animals getting intae his barley. Ah bet he hudnae counted oan snaring skiving schoolgirls, sneakin through his fields.

Ah looked down at the blood which was pouring deep red from my gowpin haund. It was the same colour as the school jersey, which had been stuffed intae ma backpack that morning – 'Burgundy wine,' the teachers ayewis said; but we just thought that was a gey fancy way of saying 'maroon'.

Maybe Ah should've just went tae the school efter aw, Ah thought tae mysel as Ah sooked the blood aff my finger.

Noo, Ah wis never a lover of the school. Ah wis bright enough, mind you, Ah just didnae get along very well wae the teachers, or the pupils for that matter. My granny had ayewis telt me, 'Wha's fur ye'll no go by ye.' Well, school definitely wisnae fur me, so Ah wis determined to let it go by me by pluggin it as often as Ah could.

Ah wis fair scunnered when Ah woke up that morning to find three giant plooks covering my forehead and chin. As if Ah didnae already look bad enough being tall and lanky, with permed hair. Ah'd ayewis had a problem wae acne, and Ah'm no just talking a few wee pimples. Mine were all red and pus-filled, like three Belisha beacons rising out of my face.

Ah tried my best to cover them with some pan stick,

but it was nae use. Sarah Harris and Kelly Muir wid have a field day if they saw me like this. They'd cry me 'pizza face' and 'polka-dot heid' whenever Ah passed them in the school corridor, and Ah didnae fancy hingin aboot tae hear what they'd come up wi next. It wid be much easier if Ah just didnae go tae school. At least that wey, Ah widnae end up greetin in front ay everyone again.

So that was it, ma mind was made up. Ah decided to get the bus intae Stirlin and spend the day shoppin instead of goin tae school. Noo, this required military-style preparation first, so's that Ah widnae get caught. Ah raided my piggy bank and counted out £2.50 worth of pocket money that Ah'd saved up, so combined wi ma dinner money Ah'd hae plenty for ma bus fare and some scran.

Ah hid the money away in my schoolbag, along wi a change of claes, just in case someone spotted my school uniform and grassed me in. If my maw asked what the claes were fur, Ah'd just tell her we had PE. Ah said cheerio to her and then hid in the woods around the corner until she'd left for work. Ah couldn't take the chance of waiting at the bus stop, in case she saw me. Ah bet she hud nae idea that Ah was so sly and sleekit.

Ah arrived in Stirlin and headed straight for the new Marches shoppin centre, which wis much better than the decrepit auld Thistles Centre. A twelve-year-auld lassie could get lost in there fur oors, and that's how Ah planned to spend the day.

Ma first stop was the Virgin Megastore to browse all the new releases. They had loads of good singles on cassette – Catatonia, Puff Daddy, All Saints – but then, Ah could ayewis just tape them aff the radio instead. And onyway, Ah had tae save my money tae get back hame again.

Ah swithered where tae go for grub – Maw wid only let

us hae a Burger King about once a year, and Ah still hudnae tried thon KFC yet. But anyone who kens Stirlin will ken that there really wis only one option, and that was the Pancake Place. My maw wid never have let me hae just pancakes for my dinner, so Ah thought Ah might as well treat mysel.

The rest of the day Ah just wandered roond the shops, surprised that naebody noticed me, or asked why Ah wisnae in school. Ah ended up in Topshop, browsin through their sale, disappointed that Ah couldnae afford tae buy anything, when Ah spotted a bargain bin, selling thong underwear for only 50p.

Thongs were all the rage back then, and some aulder lassies Ah kent fae school wore them. You could see the elastic sticking out o'er the top of their trackies. These lassies were ayewis popular at school and ayewis surrounded by huge groups of boys. Ah wondered whither the boys wid like me mair if Ah started wearing a thong.

Ah didnae even hesitate and gladly gave o'er the rest of ma money tae the sales assistant for two cheap thongs: yin purple and yin blue. Ah wis so chuffed wae masel, Ah didnae even care that Ah'd spent aw my bus fare, so wid hae tae walk seven miles back hame tae Alloa.

Panic set in once Ah reached the main road – there were so many cars driving past. What if somebody recognised me and went and clyped tae ma maw that Ah wisnae in school? Ah kent she'd huv a flakey if she found oot, so Ah hud tae get aff this busy road.

So that's how Ah ended up in the middle ay a field, wi ma finger sliced open wi barbed wire. The scar is still visible now, almost twenty years later.

As Ah reached the outskirts of Alloa, Ah put my school jersey back on and blended in again with the rest of the maroon jerseys making their way hame.

The Call Came

Audrey Biscotti

The call came at 4.56. I remember because I liked the
pattern. The rest of that day I did not like. The irony of
my 'born to sleep' nightshirt hits me as it hits the floor.
The morning more appropriately wore a coat of grey
mist and headlight pinholes tunnel the way as I drive to
your end.

We sit, I hold the massive hand of a mass that has
guided me to this point. Some nurse behind me pats my
shoulder in the rhythm of your last breaths. Each pat
pushes you further into the ground.

'It's time for him to rest now, he's tired, it's time to
sleep.'

Inside I shout, 'He's fucking dying, not going to sleep.'
Outside I just sit, watching your chest's strange new beat.
Still she pats. I can hear the chink of teacups in the next
room, the universal panacea of tea and toast being
prepared.

Escaping the ceremony, finding some excuse, I find
myself kissing goodbye the eyes that saw me first. I try
and dampen that coo's lick we share. I close the mouth
that gave me words. Now you have that look – the little
twisted smile when you were annoyed with me.

The sparkly fingers of a new day try to grab at the
edges of the drawn curtains. Crisp white sheets lie still
and tight over your body. My hand slips into your hand.
I touch the ridges on your nails, like mine. Dad, I need to
tell you something. It was me.

It was me who played chap door run and scared old
Mrs Smith. It was me who took the greenhouse tomatoes

and just chucked them against the wall. I made the circle patterns on the dash of the Nissan with the cigarette lighter. I'm sorry, Dad – the plastic just smelled nice. And, Dad, I lied that day you found me sitting alone in the car. You were right – I was avoiding going home.

Slim with age and wear, your wedding band slips round and round. I slip it off and slip it on; it sits neatly in the groove of my ring finger. Dad, I don't know if you knew but I was so lonely, and I cried myself to sleep so many nights because of him. He really hurt me and made me feel small.

The corridor outside is waking up to a day of to and fro. Waiting for the handle to turn and our stolen moment to be taken away by that cup of tea. I'm sorry, Dad. I was ashamed to tell you and ask for help, but I need you to know your little gifts and words made all the difference. Without knowing it you made me brave.

Removing an eyelash from a still-warm cheek and blowing it away, I make a wish. Dad, I want you to know I have found someone new. I thought I still had plenty of time to tell you. Kissing it, I let your hand go, letting you go. I turn the ring on my finger, take it off and return it to a hand that caught me whenever I fell.

The Rael Reet o the Problem

Diane Anderson

Wheesht! A hiv a secret. Gin A tell ye, ye winnae let oan, will ye? Aye, A'm shair A can trust ye...

A dye ma hair.

Fit div ye mean ye ken? A wifie o forty-some faa isnae grey maun hae a wee tate o help, ye say? Aye, bit iss is a new thing tae me – twa year syne iss colour wis aw ma ain. Iss is foo things fell oot...

A wis peyin fir ma hairdo a twa-three year syne faan the lassie speired at ma gin A'd nott a langer appyntment the neist time, for tae hae ma colour. Fair prood, A telt her iss wis ma natrul colour – aw ma ain, nae bottlies nor potions.

Bit, ye ken, it gaurt ma think. Awbodie A kent o aboot ma ain age did get colour pit oan, byse ae gallus quine faa hid gein natrul grey a filie syne. Wi a modren cut an her perjink claes, she looks fair braw an nae age at aw. Bit aw ither bodie yaised dye. Thon quine in the hairdresser widnae be her lane – awbodie maun jalouse thit ma hair colour wisnae ma ain! So fit did A dee bit tell awbodie ma story? Onybodie faa wid listen wis telt thit ma bonnie hair wis doon tae nature. A dinnae think A'm a blaw aw the time, bit A div like ma hair an A'm prood o't. Sae A blawed lik naebodie's business.

An then a wee filie syne Charlie, ma hairdresser, telt ma she thocht ma colour wis fadin. Gin wi didnae colour it seen, there wid be nae colour left. Did A wint tae gang grey? Weel, ma pal wis daen fine wi hers. Ma mither-in-law his hid fite hair, bonnie snawie fite hair, syne ivver A kent her. An she maun hae been aboot ma age faan A first met her (thon's fit happens faan ye find yer man young an haud oan tae him). Bit A wis near shair ye dinnae inherit fae yer guid-mither. Richt eneuch, ma grannie hid fite hair tae: affa bonnie an saft. Bit fit if mine didnae gang like thon? An foo lang wid it tak? Saat an pepper's a verra weel. Bit saat an ginger? Nae sae fine.

Charlie promised ma A wid hae nae fash wi growe-back an reets needin touchin up ilka five meenits. Her colourin-loon is a clivver-like chiel faa wid gie ma back fit A wis losin, wi nivver a sowl the wiser. A grittit ma teeth an gied fir it.

Faan a leukit in the mirror A saw masel fae ten year past leukin oot at ma. Fitin fine!

So fit's ma problem? Thing is, A hinnae telt mony fowk aboot ma chynge o circumstances. So noo there's fowk faa ken it's dye – A'm ower auld fir onythin ither. There's likely fowk faa suspect it's dye – they didnae believe ma faan A telt them ither. Bit there's fowk faa think A hinnae chynged an micht hae a pictur in the attic thit's leukin a hunner, bit ma heid disnae leuk a day ower thirty!

Fit dis it matter? Aye noo yer speirin the thoosan-dollar speir. Faa cares wither ma hair is bonnie rich auburn or fite, blae or purpil? Naebodie, A dinnae suppose. There's naebodie gies a docken byse me. An fit wye div A care? A'm nae really fashed wi ma leuks, as onybodie faa kens ma his nae doot jaloused. A files dinnae leuk in the gless fae morn til nicht. At wikkeynes A files dinnae dae onythin wi ma hair, nor brush it nor gie it a thocht.

So fit's ma tiravee aboot? Weel, A'm thinkin ma rael problem is growein auld. It disnae come its lane. A'm nae takkin tae aetin the same an growein broader in the beam. A'm nae chufft thit a nicht oot fooners ma fir a wikk. It's nae fine tae ken thit ma een an ma beens are jist growein mair peely-wally.

Faan ye hear aboot the anniversary o some muckle event fae thirty year syne, A'll can tell ye aw aboot it noo – A wis there an mine it fine. A aye think they'v makkit some mistak – thon cannae be thirty year – A wis a quine, an yet A mine. Ye see, in ma heid, A'm a quine yet. A lass o twinty his nae memory o events fae twinty or thirty year syne. An though A'm twice twinty (aye, an then some), A dinnae feel it, A dinnae wint it, A hiv tae stop it gin A can.

So, A micht be nae halflin or quinie ony mair. A'm a wifie be ony definition o the wird. Bit an auld wifie? A dinnae think it. Nae jist riddy fir thon ayenoo. Bit they say saxty's the new forty. A hiv a filie afore thon, at least. Mebbie then'll be time tae let the 'shiny bitties' as Lewis (ma colourist – wheesht) cries them, win throwe.

Or then, dinnae let oan aboot ma hair. Dinnae tell onybodie: A'm feelin ma age!

Things of the World

Wayne Price

According to the Buddha, it's desire for the things of the world that leads us away from enlightenment and ever deeper into the false dream of material reality. And I'd add to that: sometimes it's things themselves, not just our desires for them, that lead us astray.

The binoculars were wartime issue – my great grandfather had served on HMS *Orion,* and he'd spirited them into his sea chest after his demob, along with a brass German U-boat clock, which kept perfect German time, and a German officer's dagger (more decorative than deadly, but perfect for disembowelling the teddy bears my brothers and I had grown out of). Somehow on their journey through time, long after my great grandfather's death, the binoculars had come to rest, battered but still formidably solid – all scuffed black leather and gunmetal-grey steel – in the bottom drawer of a dresser in my parents' bedroom. God knows what I'd been furtively looking for when I found them – I dread to think – but whatever it was, it vanished from my eleven-year-old mind at once. They were so heavy I had to lift them free of the clutter inside the drawer with both hands: these were no toys; they felt weighty and purposeful as adulthood itself. I should have known they'd be trouble.

My older brother and I shared a bedroom in the attic of our small terraced house. There was no insulation between the plasterboard walls and the old slate tiles of the roof, so in the winter we froze, waking to frost patterns on the skylight and low ceiling where our breath had smoked up through the night, and in the summer, on sunny days, we could hardly bear to climb the ladder and poke our heads into the burning room. It was the summer holidays when I found the binoculars.

A small skylight looked out from the attic over our scruffy back garden. Not just our patch of grass, but the equally ratty strips of our close-packed neighbours. The skylight was near the apex of the sloping roof, and to look out of it comfortably, particularly with several pounds of Royal Navy steel and glass in my sweating hands, I needed the extra elevation of my rickety bedside table. Perched and swaying like a drunken sailor in a crow's nest, I had six gardens at my mercy: nothing could happen in them without my knowledge; nothing – no one – could escape my notice.

What is it that divides us into watchers and watched? I've always had a morbid horror of being observed, or photographed, or made the centre of attention, and could never understand how some of my friends relished those things. I don't know, but in my own case I'm sure it's partly bad conscience – some splinter of buried guilt or shame I can't remember the source of or explain – and maybe too just something that goes along with being a writer; an instinct to stay peripheral and take note of things, rather than to take part.

I don't know if Helen Haywood, the girl next door, was more comfortable as watcher or watched, but that summer she was watched, watched and watched again, whether she cared to be or not.

In all truth it wasn't a sexual thing. I admired Helen Haywood from afar, but mainly because of her offbeat, laconic way of seeing the world and expressing things. Once, on the school bus, I'd overheard her complaining wistfully to another sixth former about the boredom of taking a bath: 'nothing to do except lie there and see how far you can fit your big toe up the tap'; and once, again on the bus, she'd been accused by some heckling little boys of breaking wind and without a pause had dreamily corrected them with: 'ladies don't fart – the fairies take them away for us'.

Of course it *mattered* that she was a girl and several years older than me – older girls were a deep, inscrutable mystery, and I watched her playing catch with her small brother on their lawn, or gossiping on the garden bench with her schoolmates, or sunbathing in a rather baggy one-piece swimsuit with all the intense absorption of an astronomer – but there was nothing erotic about it in any simple sense. The excitement was to do with a new and strange kind of power; the power to be in her company in an almost godlike way: intimately close, as if I'd left my body, escaped my embarrassed, awkward otherness as a curious young boy and could hover like a trusted friend just inches from her all-but-grown-up presence; soundless, invisible, inescapable (at least until she got bored and sauntered back indoors).

I don't know how many days or even weeks I spent like this, balanced at the top of the house on a trembling pedestal, in an oven-like heat, but when it finally ended, my power was broken suddenly, like a spell, and like spells in fairy tales it was broken by reversal.

As she often did, Helen was sitting and reading, and occasionally picking her nose, on a concrete step in front of the ugly breeze-block garage that filled the back of the Haywoods' garden. I hadn't once seen her father all the time I'd been spying on her – he was a miner and would have been down the pit during the day, of course – but this afternoon he was at home for some reason and must have been working in the garage without my knowing it. To this day I wonder how it was that the first thing he looked at as he stepped through the garage door was me, or rather the sinister sight of two black barrels poking ominously through a propped-up skylight. Maybe the glass of the lenses had flashed in the sun and alerted him. I'd focused on him as he strode from the garage door and stood over his daughter, and when he pointed straight at me, and moved his lips in some kind of warning or exclamation, the abrupt, magnified gesture was like the long finger of God poking me in the eye. I fell backwards as if shot, the bedside table clattering through the attic hatch and breaking its legs on the landing below. My spine thumped onto the bed frame so heavily I still get twinges from where it bruised half a lifetime on.

And along with my fall, but falling the opposite way, like one half of an apple cut in two, the watchable world I thought I could observe and gain knowledge of fell also. It toppled back into the dream that the binoculars had seemed to make as solid as themselves, as real and close by, but that was always out of reach, in fact, and always would be.

Open Letter to Saul

M A Toothill

Dear Saul*,

As I write I ponder whether this will signify anything to you at all. You may not even recall it, but on that mythical day, I know you saw me do it. I saw you see me do it.

You remember when we were kids and every Sunday, August to May, concerned football? Sunday League Kids' Football. If we played at home the pitch was in walking distance of our houses. When we played away, a convoy of parents drove us the ten to twenty miles to the game. Our team wasn't really ever very good. You had excellent innate talent, and I had a dogged consistency and monotonously robotic game that hid my natural ineptitude, but the team as a whole was very bad. Typically our parents drove ten to twenty miles to see us smashed repeatedly at the hands and feet of bigger boys with hairier legs.

Our team, and parents, put a particular onus on the friendly and social aspects of football. I think we can both see this now as our parents' considerate, cushioning, euphemistic way of focusing us on these aspects because it was clear to them that our team would never be burdened by the pressure of success on the field. I am appreciative of my involvement in our team and the valuable lessons in teamwork under fire, problem solving under fire, and the ability to lose gracefully. Repeatedly. Under fire.

I mean to draw your mind to a particular dreaded opponent: Tame Ash FC, whose pitch was surrounded by rows upon rows of quality, high-yielding, child-enticing, energy-sapping, beautiful big conker trees. Our parents, wise to this potential distraction, set out earlier for this match due to the inevitable half an hour it would take for us to cease pelting the poor trees with sticks and branches on arrival. This was to make room for the ten allotted minutes of substandard stretching and warming-up followed by a spirited but ultimately contradictory team talk. I don't mean to target the coaching staff, your father did an excellent job – but just to express that his task was akin to making a silky football team out of a sow's ear.

The conkering at Tame Ash FC was, you must recall, always a prosperous endeavour and a vigorous upper-body warm-up. I recall fondly those times against Tame Ash FC. The times on the pitch facing Tame Ash I recall less fondly, as they were rough and distressing, but I meant the rampant conkering that could occur before these prolonged drubbings.

This particular day – which I'm sure you'll remember, once I highlight it with great specificity – saw us change into our kits in the cars (there were no changing rooms there) before storming the conker trees without mercy; all fourteen of us, the first eleven and the three subs, making a fifty-yard jog to the pitch last around twenty minutes. Even the opposing team joined the pre-game conkering, although at a distance, guardedly. I had had some minor successes, but this particular day the detection of sticks with enough heft to bring down conkers was unusually difficult. As mentioned, I possess a dogged consistency and adaptability and, not to be deterred, I explored alternative and more unconventional missiles. I was thrilled by the discovery of a large but thin chunk of tarmac about the size of one folded slice of bread or a large, double chocolate bar like a Drifter or a

Twix. You and I shared that look – I know you remember that look – a look that said 'just throw it, to hell with the consequences', and I pelted that chunk of dark road stone high towards the nearest low-hanging fruit.

We played in a blue kit, but the boy running underneath the boughs of that horse-chestnut tree wore a white kit. I have a very stark, clear image in my mind that he was wearing white. The tarmac hadn't really dislodged more than a few leaves on its way down, taking a few deviations on branches, before striking the boy with the most resounding *tok*! sound that I have ever heard. I know you remember the *tok*!, Saul. It sounded like opening a coconut with a drywall hammer or the claw part of a claw hammer. The rich *tok*! noise of finally smashing through the husky layer to the sweet fruity meat and cooling milk inside. The boy in white was clearly stunned and reeling when he looked me dead in the eyes (knowingly?) before a thickening gloop of blood cascaded down his face like red spiders' legs and interwove with his tears.

I want to thank you for never informing on me about that incident. As you may recollect, we won that match – scrappily, but we won. One of their best players had been dashed to hospital for several stitches and a suspected concussion. Now, I could not have targeted their best player anymore than I targeted the crown of his head from twenty feet away, but I feel that, as an adult, I would act more honourably than pretending not to notice that he was clearly injured. As an adult I hope that I would not have hurled the tarmac in the first place but, being a pragmatist, I feel that having hurled the tarmac and struck the boy, I would do what any normal adult would do and administer help whilst feigning ignorance of the origin of the tarmac.

Thank you for being a friend to me in a dark time when I thought myself a possible murderer who would learn after the match that I was a wanted bludgeoner and murderer and caver-in of skulls. If it had come to that, I would not have expected you to maintain your silence as you did – not with the inevitable murder investigation. But hold it you did and, as no serious legal repercussions befell me, you became a symbol of strength and solidity, and the contentedness of a guiltless man.

Honourably,

Your friend,

M

* Names changed

The Ten Confessions of Juno Dawson

Juno Dawson

The first secret was Dad
And Extra Strong Mints
Mum and Minnie Mouse in Florida
'I'll see you on a weekend
We'll get ice cream and candyfloss.'
Adulterer.

The second secret was Mum
Gingerbread women
Four divorcées
Eight kids in neon cycling shorts
Burn on the Costa Del Sol
Aquapark.

The third secret was Her
Chopping Board Girl
Razor blade Pink Lady
Adopting the waifs and strays and queers
Nature's hated children
Adolescence.

The fourth secret was James
He liked arms and shoulders
Broad backs and beards
Business suit sugar daddies
Superman and super men
Asexual.

The fifth secret was Jon
Marlboro Lights
A kiss by the pier
Cheap warm white wine
Your dreams of boys and girls
Awakening.

The sixth secret was Him
Boys and toys, boys as toys
I loved you
You loved the idea of me
Pistachio ice cream at Morocco's
Affliction.

The seventh secret was Love
Obsession, boiling red
Both hands on the hob
Blistered and burnt and betrayed
You look so fine, still do
Ache.

The eighth secret was You
You threw my hedgehog on the ceiling
Proud to be yours in the supermarket
Guinea pigs
Love doesn't have to hurt
Affection

The ninth secret was Then
You lie like it's breathing
Lost Boy
Happy Families in Wendy houses
But I'm glad you're happy with Massimo, honestly
Alienation.

The tenth secret was Juno
All or nothing, nothing or all
The plug in the sink
She knew
The call was coming from inside the house
Affirmation.

Presto Pronto

Jane Swanson

Anyone visiting our house in the early '70s couldn't have failed to notice a red-orange stain splattered on the dining-room wall. Like an abstract painting, the stain was made up of drizzles, splashes and drips. However hard we scrubbed, the stain wouldn't come off, and the wall had to be repainted. I have to confess that the stain was my doing.

Back then we spent our summer holidays in Rimini in Italy. My parents were friends with an Italian family who lived close by in the mountains. We visited at the weekends and whilst the grown-ups chatted, my younger sister and I spent time with Nonna: Grandma.

Nonna was short and stout and smiley with a soft wrinkled face and wispy white hair. She dressed in black and wore black tights and black lace-up shoes. She spoke no English and we knew very little Italian, but with laughter and simple gestures we understood each other. After a time, we learnt some of her Italian phrases and she learnt the English translations. She would cup our faces in her gnarled old hands and tell us we were her *angeli* - angels.

The ground floor of the house was Nonna's kitchen. It had double doors, which opened onto the street, and an ancient wood-fired range with a large oven. The room was dark and smoky; when the wind blew tiny pieces of bark scuttled across the stone floor like an army of cockroaches. Besom brooms made from bundles of twigs and hand-plaited straw bushes lay propped up against the far wall. To a child it was like being in the witch's kitchen from the story of Hansel and Gretel, and I have to confess that I was a little wary of the roaring oven. When it was time to eat and we were seated at the dining table, I felt a childish sense of relief that my sister and I had escaped being eaten.

In the middle of the kitchen there was a large table covered in a grey oilcloth where Nonna rolled out the pasta dough with a giant rolling pin. Sometimes, under her watchful eye, we were allowed to help. We rolled the smooth lump of dough out from the centre, one way at a time, until it was thin and stretchy. Sometimes, Nonna would cut it into squares and make ravioli. Sometimes she used the edge of the rolling pin as a ruler and would cut the pasta into long ribbons. We liked it best when she made ribbons because she'd wiggle her hips and dance across the floor to show us how perfectly cooked pasta ribbons should move across a plate like little snakes.

When Nonna filled the pan with water she added plenty of salt and would say, 'The cooking water needs to taste like the sea.' Whilst the pasta was cooking, Nonna would warm the sauce in a pan. When the pasta was ready, there was no time to lose and we knew to be quiet. Nonna drained the pasta and put it in a large bowl. The process of mixing the pasta and the sauce was fast and furious; the pasta was flipped and spun until each ribbon was coated in a glossy layer of sauce. As she worked, she muttered, '*Presto pronto,*' soon ready, and when she was finished we'd race upstairs to the dining room. Nonna's pasta had a silky texture, a soft yellow hue and a rich eggy flavour.

Once, after a visit to Italy, my parents invited Dad's boss and his wife over for an Italian meal. I must have been about eleven or so. My sister and I were bundled into our nightdresses and brought downstairs to meet the guests. Mum placed a steaming dish of spaghetti Bolognese in the centre of the table.

'I picked up a good tip when we were in Italy. If you add a couple of tablespoons of the cooking water when mixing the pasta and the sauce, the starch in the water helps the sauce to stick to the pasta. In Italy, they call it the marriage between the pasta and the sauce. The starch works like glue and, like in any marriage, you need a bit of glue to hold things together, don't you!' said Mum.

The grown-ups laughed.

'I find the best way to check if spaghetti is cooked is to take a piece out of the pan and bite it. If it's hard in the middle then that means it's not ready,' said the boss's wife.

I'm still not sure to this day why I did what I did next. Perhaps it was to show off that I had been to Italy and knew a little about cooking? Perhaps I was disgruntled at being packed off to bed. Or maybe it was just pure spite. I reached across the table and pulled a small handful of spaghetti out of the bowl.

'I'll show you how Nonna knows if the spaghetti is ready,' I said.

'You're not supposed to do it with the sauce on!' screamed my sister.

Too late. I flung it at the wall. The spaghetti sped towards it like a low flying jet and hit it with a soft plop like a stone dropped in water without making a splash. The spaghetti stuck, a perfect little snake surrounded by red-orange splatters and a smattering of minced beef. Like a Jackson Pollock painting in the making, dribbles of sauce slithered down the magnolia wall.

I Must Confess What I Like the Best!

David Gilchrist

'Aye'
Friday
McDonald's
Yip!
Car
Malkie
3 o'clock
'Aye'
Burger

I See Ghosts

M J Petrie

My secret confession is: 'I see ghosts; a closet clairvoyant
    am I.'
I talk to the dead and the dying, you see; I talk to them
    and they talk to me.
Since I was a child I have seen ghosts; they're just like
    you and I.
They come to tell their stories and show me how they died.
When I was two, I could see an invisible world in front of
    me.
Sitting outside in my pram, the spirits and ghosts did me
    no harm.
My granny read the tea leaves and shared what she could
    see.
Her predictions were uncanny, but she never took a fee.
When I was young, I used to play with spirit friends
    every day.
When I went out, I'd see ghosts there; I'd see them almost
    everywhere.
Sometimes they would pass me by; some would laugh
    and some would cry.
Others, they would speak to me; they'd ask directions,
    say 'Good day',
or tell me what they had to say, to pass to loved ones
    when I may.
I have seen ghosts throughout my youth; at first I shared
    my vision,
but I was told I must not tell; and that was their decision!
They said folk would not understand; they'd say I was a
    witch.

They said I had to pray for help, and I should join the
    church.
For many years, I told no one when I talked to the dead.
I dared not share their messages, and cried at night in
    bed.
Growing up, I still saw ghosts, but I became afraid,
of what to say, or who to tell; frustration filled my head.
When I left home, the ghosts came too; I saw them
    everywhere.
They asked me for my help again; they asked me if I cared.
I said, 'I did, I do, I will.' I said, 'I'll do my best.'
I asked for visits in daytime; at night I had to rest.
They agreed and thanked me, for helping them once more.
Throughout the years, so many ghosts came knocking at
    my door.
Some were children, lost in time; who needed help and
    spoke in rhyme.
Ethereal beings also visit, with wisdom they wish to
    share.
They help me in my daily life and really seem to care.

Haunted homes, persistent ghosts, forced me once again.
I was the flame and they the moths; they saw me as their
    friend.
I'd listen to them and find out why they chose to hang
    around.
I'd do my best to help them then tell them when I'd
    found;
their loved ones, lost in limbo, if they were still around.

I see ghosts and hear them; I speak to them at home.
They call me up and ask for help, on the psychic telephone.
Spirits often visit; some family and friends.
All of them have words to share, or love they wish to send.

I have a portal on my stair, I hear a tune, and ask, 'Who's
    there?'
Most spirits say, 'Hallo, it's me, there's something I would
    like to say.'
'Please tell my wife I'm worried; she needs to check
    things out.
She needs to see the doctor; of that I have no doubt.
Her health, you see, is important, I love her very much.
Please tell her not to be afraid; that God will shine his
    torch…'
'…It's Dad here; I've brought Granny through.
We want to say we're proud of you.'

I'm not ashamed of who I am, I see, and hear, and touch;
Your loved ones who've passed over; they love you very
    much.
Bringing comfort, peace and hope; they help you with
    your pain to cope.
Inspiration, they also bring; the children have a bell they
    ring.
I am clairvoyant, this is true; most people, though, don't
    have a clue.
No longer hiding who I am, I'm out, and I am proud;
I'll tell the world, that I SEE GHOSTS! and SHOUT IT
    VERY LOUD!

Your Call or Mine?

Jeni Rankin

My friend Helen has a secret and, in telling me, she's made it mine too. I wish she hadn't because now it feels like a burden. Try as I might, I can't unhear what she said and can't unknow what I learned.

We'd met as usual at Julie's in Oban, selecting our favourite table and enjoying the mixed aromas of coffee and sweet cakes. After our usual blethering to catch up, Helen had leaned forward and put her hand over mine.

'Alice, there's something I'm bursting to tell you,' she said. I smiled and wondered briefly if she was pregnant.

'I'm having an affair,' she whispered in an excited and conspiratorial tone. I must have looked shocked because she sat back in her chair. 'You don't approve.'

'I'm... I'm just surprised,' I said, struggling to sound reassuring and not judgemental. 'I had no idea.'

I suppose, looking back, I'd been blind to the clues: the slimmer figure, the change of hairstyle, an animation in her manner; but I would never have suspected this. I became aware that Helen was leaning forward, talking again and, as she trod on the fragile eggshells of truth, I learned how they met, connected and stepped into this dangerous dance.

'But what about Derek?' I found myself asking.

'Oh God, he doesn't know and he mustn't find out! You must never tell him.' Helen emphasised this by again covering my hand with hers. And there it was – I was drawn into her secret.

As we sat, Helen talked about her lover, his smile, his eyes, the way he dressed, it struck me that she sounded like a lovesick teenager. I tried to give the right responses and reactions, but my mind was already on a different track.

We were interrupted by her ringtone and, judging by the giggling and flirting, this was her lover. It gave me time to ponder; I never thought Helen would have an affair because her husband Derek is so nice. I really like him. We all do – he's funny, romantic and kind. We were all delighted when they threw in their lot together. But, apparently, he's not romantic, funny or kind enough for her now, she's looked elsewhere. Although the man she'd just told me about didn't sound as nice as Derek, maybe she's attracted to a different, possibly darker side of him that her husband doesn't have.

When Helen eventually finished her call with whispered endearments, she unnecessarily informed me it had been her lover. We continued our chat, eventually moving away from her affair and onto sharing news of friends and family. I tried to react to her in the way I would normally, but part of me was already in a quandary. We parted having made arrangements to meet again.

As I wandered away I couldn't stop thinking about the situation. Helen and I have known each other since infant school, a friendship forged over Lego bricks, Play-Doh and paint pots and developed through exams, make-up, boyfriends and the first tastes of alcohol. We'd shared everything and always remained close wherever life took us. But this was something new. I thought, *What do I do now?* When I see Derek I won't know what to say and can anticipate being embarrassed. I don't 'do' secrets, never have, and I don't like lying to people, even by omission. If he sees my embarrassment, will he guess?

In the weeks since Helen first told me, things have got worse. She phoned last week and said she'd told Derek she'd been with me on Tuesday when she was with her lover. She's asked me to cover for her if it comes up with Derek. I was horrified; it felt like one of those dreams where you're dragged unwittingly onto the dance floor, even though you don't know the steps.

As if that wasn't bad enough, Helen phoned again yesterday and told me she's going to see her lover on Wednesday, and she's told Derek she's going to be with me, and to give her an alibi if he happens to call. I can feel myself being pulled ever deeper into Helen's dissembling, like being sucked into the swirling depths of a whirlpool. I feel trapped by her lies. This isn't my life, it's hers, but she's making it mine.

I feel as if Helen's stretching the bonds of friendship too far, but I also think she'll be hurt if I say no. In her somewhat selfish pursuit of her adventure she's blind to what it's doing to me. I'm hurt that she wants to drag me into her subterfuge. I'm not judging her – it's her life and she must live it as she may – but she's forced me unwittingly to become part of the deception.

I don't know what to do. My mind's whirling with the strain of it all and words are buzzing in my head: 'lies', 'deceit', 'suspicion', 'alibi', 'cover-up'. Other words like 'truth', 'exposure' and 'confession' are also drumming in my skull. If I refuse to cooperate will I mortally wound our friendship? That would hurt me a great deal, but then I think Helen has pushed the limits of friendship to breaking point. I've also thought a lot about Derek; I can't help but feel immensely sorry for him in his innocence of this cheating. I've had to keep this secret from my own husband because I know, unbound by friendship with Helen, he would tell Derek in an instant. I've even been tempted to tell Derek myself, but that would feel like betraying Helen, and it's difficult to be the bearer of such devastating news. The consequences of either of those courses of action are intolerable to me.

And yet here I am, sitting by the phone about to make a call. Who shall I call and what shall I say to them?

Unspoken

Chiew-Siah Tei

It was late October.

That morning the azaleas bloomed, a brilliant red against the whitewashed walls outside the hospital ward. Inside, the last drops of the saline still dripped along the tube that had been turned off, so that they were unable to find their way into your body.

I had just walked out from the ward. The sun had risen early, already glaring. I shielded my eyes with a hand, squinting. I had forgotten how bright, how fiery the tropical sun could be. I had forgotten my dark glasses, my parasol, my sun lotion.

In fact, I had forgotten many things, Mother. I had forgotten the cups of rich, steamy Milo on the breakfast table early morning to see us, the children, off to school every day. I had forgotten how you had hunched over your old Singer, night after night in the dim gaslight, to conjure up one item after another: my day dresses, school uniforms, pyjamas. I had forgotten also the peonies and chrysanthemum on my pillowcases, the fine threads of toned red and green on pale linen. I did not know then, into the cups of the hot beverage, into every piece of the garments, you quietly stirred or stitched a secret in codes you would never reveal, only waiting to be decoded by us.

I had forgotten too many things, Mother. I could have blamed my years of being a wanderer, of living in a cold country – the chill winds, a fourteen-hour flight between us, half a globe away – but could I?

The truth is, I had chosen to remember instead the red,

swollen marks of caning on my calves, the burning sensation that seeped into my young flesh. How the minds trick us, Mother. The memories of pain always preside over those more worthy, deeper feelings.

I was young then, too young to comprehend your rage, to reason and find out the source of it. In my childish mind, I was the cause of your anger. I did not know then the culprit was the centuries-old corrupt beliefs of an ancient culture. Confucianism, so it is called. Those beliefs were ingrained in Grandpa, in Father – as in the generations of men before them – so that it was right, to them, to load you down with endless chores, endless demands in voices loud and stern. And like the women of your generation and beyond, you bowed your head low and took them all in. Inside you, though, they rumbled, those orders and reprimands, growing into a resentment that would burst into fury. That would then be transferred to the cane you picked up – when I came home late from an afternoon of basketball games in school; when my clumsy hands dropped a plate, a bowl, a cup; when I was too slow at folding away the garments you'd sewn for a local shop for extra cash. Your anger shifted to me, through the stick you lashed onto my body. It drove us apart.

I had also chosen to be a wanderer: drifting away from home, away from you. It was such a delight that year, when I finally left the southern town for the university on a small island in the far north. With that move, a line was irrevocably drawn between us. In a place where my past was unknown to all, I was thrilled to open the door to a different realm: new activities, new friends, new knowledge. The distance further widened with my subsequent relocations, for work or studies, from Penang to Kuala Lumpur and, later, Glasgow, a city so alien that even to have a glimpse of it in the world news was rare. My occasional letters and postcards failed to bring to life the seasons, the lochs and rivers, and to tell the stark difference between the barren bens and the dense, luxuriant tropical forests.

You had never had an insight into my world.

Over the years, I travelled to places with people and cultures beyond my knowledge. In Siklis, a hilltop dwelling in Nepal, I danced with the villagers in a ceremony to honour the head of the village's seventieth birthday. On another hilltop, this time a remote town in Sicily, Palazzolo Acreide, I paced the street lined with volcanic stones and recollected the history and the cultures, retracing the footsteps of the Greeks, the Romans, the Arabs, the Normans and the Spanish. Another time, in another ancient city with a culture I originated from, I tried to visualise my ancestors' journey. I saw them trudging westwards from an inland mountainous village in the south to the port city before embarking on a turbulent ride across the South China Sea. It was then memories of the past began to resurface.

I had left home long enough ago then. My teenage angst had long subsided. Wandering in a foreign place at times unsettled me. From one place to another, regardless of where I was, something was inherently missing. I was an outsider peeping into others' homes. There was never a door to enter into. There was never another pair of eyes to look back at me.

Somewhere inside me, though, I knew where I could find that gaze I longed for.

My last day in Szechuan that fated autumn, as I drifted along the paths lined with long stalks of bamboo, the news came to me. You had fallen off your wheelchair, blood clogging in your brains. It had been seven days.

That night, I sat by your bed in the hospital, watching closely as you drifted in and out of consciousness. I wanted to talk to you. I wanted to tell you I had decoded your secret. I wanted to ask if you knew mine, too, but instead I began to recite a mantra of compassion in a low murmur.

You opened your eyes and, for a few moments, you gazed at me.

I know. You blinked.

I wrapped your hand in mine.

Yes, Mother. I know, too.

Sàmhchair
Silence

Marcas Mac an Tuairneir

Cha do dh' iarr mi thu mar nàmhaid,
B' urrainn dhut a bhith nam charaid,
Nam faiceadh tu tron cheò
Mud choinneamh.

Dh'iarr thu orm co-choslachadh,
Cha b' urrainn dhomh mo thàmhachadh,
Cha chluinneadh tu an ceò,
Na mo ghuth.

'S e seo an cogadh na thost;
An strì eadar iomadach loidhne
Agus stadaidh sinn an seo oir,
Cha do ghabh thu idir ri mo dhòighean.

Aghaidh ri aghaidh san talla;
Chan eil air fhàgail ach sàmhchair
Nach gabhar a gleusadh.
Tha sinn nar crìonglaich
A' chogaidh shàmhaich seo.

Cha do dh' iarr mi thu mar nàmhaid,
B' urrainn dhut a bhith nam charaid,
Nan tiodhlaiceadh ar sabaid
Anns an uaigh.

Mura miste leat mi a ràdh,
Bheirinn maitheanas dhut gu bràth,

Nan aidicheadh tu coire
Na rinn thu.
'S e seo an cogadh na thost;
An strì eadar iomadach loidhne
Agus stadaidh sinn an-seo oir,
Cha do ghabh thu idir ri mo dhòighean.

Aghaidh ri aghaidh san talla;
Chan eil air fhàgail ach sàmhchair
Nach gabhar a gleusadh.
Tha sinn nar crìonglaich
A' chogaidh shàmhaich seo.

* * *

I didn't call you to be my enemy,
You could have been a friend,
If you'd but see through the brume
Before you.

You called me to assimilate,
I'm not the type for respite,
You were deaf to the amazement
In my voice.

So this is the silent war;
The struggle between myriad lines
And our stalemate stands between us,
As you couldn't embrace my little ways.

Face to face in the auditorium;
Nothing but the silence
That can't be fine-tuned.
The culprits paired in

This, our silent war.

I didn't call you to be my enemy,
You could have been a friend,
If you'd interred our quarrel
In the sepulchre.

If you don't mind me saying,
I'd forgive you every time,
If you'd admit your part
In the matter.
So this is the silent war;
The struggle between myriad lines
And our stalemate stands between us,
As you couldn't embrace my little ways.

Face to face in the auditorium;
Nothing but the silence
That can't be fine-tuned.
The culprits paired in
This, our silent war.

Superglue and Tights

Rab B

When I was about eleven years old I did something that still makes me laugh to this day.

My younger brother was getting lippy with me and acting smart, so I decided to pay him back.

He was acting in his school play as a fairy tree, and he was really looking forward to the show. His costume was brown tights, a dark green leaf skirt, a lighter green top and branches with green leaves attached to his arms.

He asked me to go and get his tights and I decided to put superglue inside the tights. I squeezed the whole tube inside the legs and gave them to him. He started to put them on but complained they were a bit damp. Quick as a flash I said, 'Yeah, Mum just washed them – that's why they're damp.'

'Oh okay. They'll be dry before I get to the school,' he said, and off he went to the show.

When he came home he went upstairs to get changed and I heard him shout, 'Why can't I get these bloody tights off?'

He came downstairs and took one look at me. I was giggling.

'You did something!' he shouted at me.

'Who, me?' I said through the giggles.

I confessed, 'I put superglue in your tights to get you back for being lippy.'

'I was only joking,' he said.

He went upstairs to get the tights off. They were stuck fast to his skin, so he went to the bathroom and found my dad's razor. He opened up the old-fashioned razor and took the blade out, then he tried to cut the tights off his leg.

Unfortunately, he slipped and sliced into the flesh below his knee. He had to go to the hospital to get some stitches.

I had been laughing, but then I felt a bit bad – I didn't mean for him to get hurt. I must admit he wasn't quite as lippy to me again though.

The Onion Ceremony

Glenn Robinson

Everyone in my third-year chemistry class wanted to do
well. Everyone wanted to do well for the wrong reason.
Our teacher, Barney Rubble as he was known, had a
curious way about him. We would imagine that he
travelled to school caveman style, using his feet to power
his old banger. His hair was unkempt, his shirt half
hanging out and his white coat, denoting his mad-
scientist status, was always carrying some form of
mysterious stain. On paper, he could claim to be a
scientist. How he behaved, however, was a lot less
enlightened. He practised some form of religion that
none of us had ever heard of.

We had a class test every few weeks and no one ever
wanted to come last. The boy that came last became The
Onion. To be anointed The Onion meant going through a
process of ritual humiliation. The process itself was an
open secret between the boys and the teacher. Nobody's
parents ever found out. None of the other teachers
seemed to be aware of what was happening.

With the class test marked, Mr Rubble asked the class
to guess who The Onion was. The guessing was a form of
torture. If my name came up, it meant that at least
someone thought I was stupid. If others agreed, my pain
was multiplied. If a second name came up, others would
debate the demerits of each of us. With common cruelty,
it was a raucous affair with much laughter and teasing.
Our leader, Mr Rubble, was much encouraged.

He would tease the class further by reading the names
of the boys who finished in the top half. The rest of us,

who remained unnamed, sat silently hoping that we would not be The Onion. The guessing continued. If I managed to do well enough to finish in the top half of the class, I would feel a sense of relief and become desensitised to the plight of the poor sod who would eventually become the subject of ridicule. The majority would become winners while the runt of the class was destroyed without mercy.

The guessing continued. The class were asked to reassess who they thought The Onion might be. On the occasion I became The Onion, no one guessed my name. I sat silently hoping that I had done enough to escape the clutches of the class mob.

Finally, when it was announced that I had come last, I was summoned to the front of the room. I was asked to kneel in front of the teacher and a white polystyrene box was placed upside down on my head. The box had on the side of it the names of all the previous Onions, with the dates of their enthronement.

I was asked to stand and to slowly make my way around the room. The boys were split into two, sitting at the side of two long benches in the science lab. My course of humiliation took me on a figure of eight. I took off to the left before twisting around to the bottom of the class, making my way up to the centre of the room towards Barney Rubble. The boys all chanted, 'Onion, Onion, Onion.' They seemed to imply that if they peeled a layer of skin from my head, they would find another layer and then yet another. If they continued to peel, they would never find a brain. As I approached the teacher, I was told to slow down, before I swept off to the right, taking on the other half of the room. The chanting continued. 'Onion, Onion, Onion.'

When I approached Barney Rubble again, I knelt back

down onto one knee to repeat The Onion oath. Mr Rubble suggested to everyone that he knew Swahili, and that the oath would be conducted in this most sacred of languages.

'Repeat after me,' he said.

'Oswa.'

'Oswa.'

'Wassia.'

'Wassia.'

'Iama.'

'Iama.'

Turning to the boys, Barney Rubble asked what I had just said. They shouted back, 'Oh, what an ass I am!'

The boys broke into a drum roll. They drum rolled on their desks for up to a minute. Before the enthusiasm of the class was exhausted, Mr Rubble signalled for the class to stop. I then stood up and The Onion hat was taken from my head. My name was placed on the box along with the date. I was asked if I would be The Onion next time. I can't remember what I replied. What I do remember is that there was never a boy who became The Onion twice. Having been on the receiving end of such ridicule and mockery, no one desired a repeat of the experience.

At the time, I never thought the ceremony was strange or unusual. It was 1989, a few years after corporal punishment was banned from state schools. No one ever told their parents that they had come last in the class test. No one boasted about becoming The Onion. As fourteen-year-olds, going to an all-boys school, we seemed to live in a sealed bubble. Our sense of normality was strange.

The Changeling

Alison Dawson

On reflection it could never happen now. These days, thanks to foot-and-mouth and BSE, every cattle beast has its own cattle passport from birth. Its breeding, distinguishing markings and date of birth are duly entered on the national database, and its every movement on or off the farm is recorded on an official movement form. Total traceability is the government mantra.

As a girl I had spent weekends and school holidays helping at a local dairy farm. Jean and Harry were childless, and while Harry was a rather dour, hard character, Jean and I were inseparable. I can still see her now, stirring pails of hen feed in her wraparound pinny and lisle stockings. Our province was mainly the hens and the dairy, and I could strip down a milking machine in jig time for the steriliser. Jean in particular had been delighted when I became engaged to a farmer, and we were bidden to come and inspect the calf from their renowned dairy herd, which was to be their very generous wedding present. She was adorable. Pure white apart from a black patch on her left side with melting brown eyes and film-star eyelashes, she was what a stockman would call a 'sappy' heifer. Fiancé Bill had a white collie with a black patch on her left side and on the way home we remarked on this coincidence.

Six months later, newly returned from our honeymoon, we went to pick up our present. Tea, scones and wedding photos later we backed the trailer up to the calf shed. The dairyman opened the pen and ushered out our calf. Bill and I exchanged dismayed glances. We didn't need the confirmation of the missing black patch on her side to know that this scrawny creature was not the same calf. I looked at Jean. She knew I knew, she knew I knew that she knew, and she knew that I knew it was not of her doing. Gracious acceptance was the order of the day. We made the right noises and drove off.

She was such an ugly specimen that I felt that the least we could do was to give her a pretty name. As Anastasia she was introduced to our herd of hardy hill cows. She never really fitted in. With her pale colour and cadaverous frame she might have been more acceptable in a back street in Mumbai. She was so lean that I spent her first winter dreading a knock on the door from the SSPCA man suspecting neglect. I soaked a stockpot of barley in the bottom of the Aga every night in an attempt to put some flesh on her bones. She survived, eventually matured and produced her first calf. In spite of her unprepossessing appearance it did indeed seem that she came from a dairy background, as she had an impressive milk yield. So much so that I was able to tuck my head into her flank and milk a foaming pail from her each morning. She was a good mother, and as her calf grew and got hungrier, she would eventually grudge my share of her largesse. There would come the morning when she kicked the bucket and refused to stand. Message received and understood – we were back to the Co-op for our milk till the next calving. The years passed and Anastasia certainly earned her keep. I even grew fond of her long, lugubrious face with the permanent 'what can't be cured must be endured' expression.

Hill farming in the west of Scotland has always been a marginal enterprise and subject to the vagaries of the market. In the mid-70s the bottom fell out of the cattle market and calf prices crashed. In an attempt to help the more remote farmers the auction market in Stirling introduced a scheme which involved taking a group of buyers round individual farms to look at the year's calf crop in situ and save the farmer wasted transport costs. The buyers got the chance to look at the dams and the general terrain where the stock was reared.

Thus we found ourselves on a crisp autumn morning strolling through our stock with five or six interested dealers and the head auctioneer from the market. Mr Scott, the auctioneer, suddenly stopped, took off his tweed cap and scratched his head.

'Bill, would you mind if I asked you where you got the white cow?'

'Actually she was a wedding present,' replied Bill, 'but I don't know for sure where she came from.'

'The mean old bugger,' mused the auctioneer, a smile beginning to spread across his face. 'You got her from Harry at Woodside on the Fife border, didn't you?'

'How on earth could you know that?' replied an astonished Bill. 'It was years ago.'

'That it was,' said the auctioneer, 'and I have often wondered since what he was up to, but the secret's out now. He was a client of the mart, mean as dirt and a great one for dodgy deals. I remember the day he came in. I couldn't work out what he was up to and he wasn't telling. All he said was that I had to find him a heifer calf. He didn't care what she looked like or where she came from, she just had to be pure white and cheap! I managed to find one that filled the bill and never expected to see her again, but I am sure that's her there. Would stake my reputation on it.'

By this time the auctioneer was in fits of laughter and regaling the buyers with his tale. Bill and I were nonplussed but of course it explained everything. The odds against that particular auctioneer being in our field looking at our stock would be hard to calculate and Harry could never have foreseen it. Ironic justice of a sort, but in retrospect we wouldn't have been without our Anastasia.

A Blessing of Frogs

Christine Laurenson

(i)
'Come and see,' my sister says, and leads
the hand-held walk, from yard to cellar door.
Green paint curls from wood in sharp petals,
the rusted latch too high for me, but she can reach
to clank and rattle. Hinges grumble, door swings
to stone steps and treacle black.

'Just wait,' she says.
My eyes are wide, stretching, seeking light;
my nose reads green water and strange herbs.
I hear faint pops and splashes. Gradually,
my eyes begin to see; moss climbs in soft drifts,
dark water throws a dance of light around the walls.

'See!' she says and points. My sister smiles.
Uncertain, I gaze at small frogs
scrabbling to escape our bright noise.

(ii)
Quivering, alone, in the school doorway,
in that thin frock, hand-me-down, outgrown,
my bare shins blossomed in bruises,
I see them hiding by the gate,
waiting for me.

Outside, the green blazes and hums,
dandelion seeds speckle the breeze and the sun-hot air
is sharp with buttercups.

Then, soft, a sudden darkening
blunts the day. Javelins of rain
spear down, sputtering on dry earth.
My tormenters shriek and flee and I wonder,
'Did it rain for me?'

It stops and I step out into the sparkle, to the top of the
    hill,
where trees crowd the lane, like gossips. There, on the
    puddled track,
a hundred frogs twitch and jitter across my path,
gifting their joy, like a sister's blessing.

Talker

Shona Cook

You'd be surprised to know I had secrets, if you met me.
Useless at eye contact, but oh I can talk. Words pour out,
unfiltered. A boyfriend once called it verbal jazz. Said he
liked to hear it, jangling in the background, but never
paid attention to the meaning.

It's a nervous tic, like chimps grinning when threatened.
I guess it sounds like openness.

Really, it's a wall.

That morass of information, inane and intimate,
amusing and harrowing, dull and grotesque, swamps
questions, extinguishes them. No one wants to know
more. No one learns the tricky stuff.

No one knows I'm a nearly-murderer.

We were used to camping holidays; Devon, Cornwall,
till longer drives were bearable, then France. Throbbing
ferries, long lanes of elegant trees, fields of sunflowers,
quiet country churches, then the rocky, precipitous
Ardèche, or Camargue's heat and white horses born
black. Ramshackle freedom of soft walls and cooking
over blue flames. Sandy toes and shared shower blocks.
Never, however, to paddle in the turbulent river or
rip-tidal ocean unsupervised.

This year was different. Menorca was the kind of
holiday other families took; echoey airport, cramped
plane, applause at landing, stark white apartments
jagged against navy sky, a swimming pool. Not private,
not exactly, but the block was small, the season early and
the blue cube empty, water unriffled. No wind or tide to

tug us out. No hidden rocks to rip at feet. No kayakers to bash us. Overlooked by our balcony. Safe.

While Mum tugged off rumpled sheets that meant the cleaners hadn't been yet, and Dad rang the rental agent, my brother and I dumped bags in the middle of the floor and pulled out costumes, desperate to shed travel's sticky cling. Dad's arm barred the way.

'Where do you two think you're going?'

'Pool.'

'We've not got time right now.'

'It's a pool. It's right outside. We're good swimmers.' A stretch. We were okay swimmers. I'd a few fabric badges and had dived for bricks, and swum in pyjamas, at school.

He wavered. We saw. Ducked beneath the arm and ran out shrieking, jumped right in. Screamed at the icy grip of it. Nobody hauled us out. Later, they joined us.

No point instituting new rules after that.

D and I could swim, so long as we were quiet during lazy siesta time and looked out for each other.

In the post-lunch lull the boys appeared. We'd seen a car arrive but thought nothing of it. D and I slithered out and dripped over to greet the interlopers, one about my age, one about his. They were English. A flash of hope we might make friends, before I knew we wouldn't. I withdrew, girl's prerogative. Fetched a book and sat on the side, legs kicking glittering droplets. Harder for D; the draw of male company, the shame of siding with a sister.

I wasn't the best big sister. Four years gave me the sharps and tools for mental cruelty, and D wasn't yet strong enough for his frustrated punches to hurt. I loved him with the passionate irritation particular to thirteen-year-olds. He was funny though, and, when no one was looking, we got on. Maybe even liked each other.

Surprising: the ferocity of my reaction when I spotted the bullying. D was laughing along, but hurt and suspicion shadowed the edges of his smile. Proprietorial at first: D was mine to torture. How dare they? Then molten anger obliterated sense. Next I knew I was balled up on the pool's rough floor tiles, arms locked round the legs of my brother's oppressor. He wasn't fighting me much, yet. I was a girl. He was bigger than me. Uncool to acknowledge I could harm him. He thought he could pull us both to the surface with just his arms. Perhaps he thought I was flirting.

The kicking came as I ran out of breath. I held on long enough to show I could. We burst through flurries of bubbles, his eyes huge, face red, movements jerky and desperate. He sloshed onto the concrete and stalked off, his confused little brother trotting behind.

After that, we only used the pool when no one else was there.

We never told our parents. I doubt D even remembers, but I do.

Sometimes, in the pool at the gym, I swim a length underwater, watch the thrashing legs and think how easy it would be. It all comes down to who can hold their breath the longest.

And I've got good lungs.

Night Call

Alexander Nicoll

The only light that dark night came from the small lamp on the front of my bike. In the blackout even little chinks of light would bring a visit from the air-raid wardens. From late September of 1939 there were obvious signs there was a war on, as Polish soldiers, survivors from Europe, had been stationed in the area. A farm servant's son, I had started secondary school in Blair the week war on Germany was declared, and all the streets were familiar territory to me. (Yes, it was just Blair to me, never the full name 'Blairgowrie'.)

Well, my schooldays were now over, and I was in employment as a farm loon. I had hopes of joining the forces and was a member of the Air Training Corps (ATC). Cars were few in those days of petrol rationing, and as I cycled along the Perth Road, the place was deserted. It was, and still is, a residential area, of large houses, with green spaces between. As I passed one of these spaces, I heard a loud female voice crying, 'Help!' I hesitated and slowed the bike. No, I thought, I won't get involved. Farm work was hard for a thin, scrawny loon like myself, and it was tiring trying to keep up with full-grown men. No, I need to get rest and sleep, I kept telling myself as I pedalled home. But an uneasy mind meant a restless night.

I did eventually join the forces and served a short period in the Royal Navy. I saw no action; the war was over before I finished my training. After demob, I had various jobs in industry, got married and had a family. In my late 30s, I embarked on a new and rewarding career in probation and social work in Dundee, which saw me through to retirement. In all these years, despite the trials and responsibilities of life, the memory of a certain night has not dimmed down. It is lurking in that wee box, out of the ken of the rest of the world.

My two daughters, both in the NHS, give unstinting help to their widowed dad in my sheltered house. We are in daily contact, and have regular outings for visits and meals. I have all that I need here, and my health is such that I rarely require to consult a doctor. I have partial deafness, though, and have hearing aids. Nevertheless, as I stare out of the back window in the direction of Blair, a call keeps repeating in my head. It is as clear as on the night I first heard it. There is no escape. It won't go away.

My Medals for Running

Lachie Johnston

I kept a secret. I didn't want to tell anyone; I wanted it to be just for me. I was in my late 30s when I took up running. It made me feel good, and I enjoyed it.

The coach's name was Willie. He was nice, and he encouraged me to get better. I exercised and trained, and I got better and faster. When Willie thought I was ready, I entered some races.

We travelled as a team in a minibus to Meadowbank in Edinburgh and to Dumbarton and to Ayr. It was exciting going to the competitions, but I was also very nervous before the start of the races.

Willie trained me well though, because I won some medals. A gold, a silver and a bronze. I felt very proud to receive my medals; I was so emotional.

After the races we would all celebrate in the pub.

The Little Red Library

Renita Boyle

The library in my hometown was a little red brick building no more than 15 feet square. It sat on a corner shading itself under the leafy oaks and elms in summer and shivered against a white arctic bareness in winter. It was as sleepy as the rural township it served in America's dairy heartland, but it woke me up to the world.

I can still recall how the screen door slammed shut behind me in the heat of a July day. Only book bugs were welcome. There were no comfy seats, no pillows, no coffee machines or computers. There was barely enough room to swing a cat in it, as folks used to say, and almost as few books as there were people in the town.

The librarian sat behind an old oak desk which was polished and pocked. Her soft silvering hair was tied back in a bun. She wore thick cat's-eye glasses, a flowery cotton dress and a smile as warm as the day. She was a retired teacher who loved children as much as she loved books.

There was no sign to keep hush, but I dared not speak. The library felt as sacred as a Sunday morning. The only sound was the soft whirring hum of an electric fan, the occasional creak of the librarian's chair and a cricket chirruping somewhere among the shelves tall as August corn stalks.

How I loved the smell of them; books from floor to ceiling standing to attention in regimented rows. Those for the young were within easy reach.

However, I often found myself on tiptoe wandering among exotic titles about places I longed to go. These broadened the horizons of a whole new world for a dairy farmer's daughter whose biggest weekly adventure was a trip to the library.

Only two books could be taken out at a time. I'd bask in the experience of choosing them even as many of my friends basked on the beach at the local lake. I'd finger their spines, dip in and out of their blurbs and wade knee-deep into first chapters before taking the plunge.

When the choice had finally been made, I'd carry my books to the librarian. She would meet my gaze with knowing eyes; as if she were an accomplice in my escape from boredom, loneliness, sorrows and secrets that, even as an adult, I am still too young to bear.

Did she know? Could she sense how I would absorb alternative realities; create happier endings for myself; new beginnings in far-off places?

She'd open the back cover of each book, remove the stained manila card from the pocket and I would add my name to the generations of familiar names before me. Then she'd roll her date stamp in deep blue ink. Click-stamp, click-stamp, the books were mine for two whole weeks.

I have long been away from all that I knew as a child. The librarian is gone now and so too is the little red library, though the building remains. And yet, I confess, I often return there in the heat of life; when bored, or lonely or in need of escape from sorrows and secrets too many to bear.

I Didn't Usually Tell People

Bruce Lumsden

I didn't usually tell people, I was in denial.
It sometimes felt like a disease and was always a trial.
Once you've caught it, there's no going back - it's going to
    last forever.
You'll feel elated or depressed, or both in equal measure.

I couldn't find a remedy, no medicine, nor potion.
It's testosterone, adrenaline and every human emotion.
Long term there were years when it slipped into remission.
Then back it came, to bite my bum, without asking for
    permission.

I longed for relief, to ease the pain, to make it go away,
but every year it grew and grew, until that fateful day.
I couldn't face it, I was scared and hid myself in shame.
I didn't want to be there, to grin and bear the pain.

It's over now thank goodness, I can walk the streets with
    pride.
No more dodging into doorways, no necessity to hide.
I can hold my head up proudly, I can speak about the past.
I can sleep soundly in my bed - Hibs have won the cup at
    last.

The Feminist

Emma Raymond

My body is covered in hair. In some places it is thin and almost white, barely visible, like on my upper arms and between my breasts. In others it is black and coarse and grows like a weed, untameable and unwelcome.

I try to keep it at bay, by plucking, waxing, shaving and melting it off with a special cream that burns the skin if left on too long. But it always comes back. I've heard about permanent solutions, something called electrolysis, but it costs hundreds of pounds that I don't have. So I keep on, resolute, with my never-ending rituals.

But it is a losing battle; dark pinpricks of hair are always visible on my calves, and my armpits are scratchy to the touch, like sandpaper. My bikini line is never quite 'beach ready'.

The feminist in me longs to let it grow free, to throw away my razor and never waste another minute plucking, or another penny on wax strips. But the insecure girl rules, and she is repelled by the sight of it. She longs for the impossibly smooth, tanned skin of a Victoria's Secret model.

I've calculated how many hours I've wasted on hair removal in my life so far: 930. Hours I could have been writing, or studying for my degree, or relaxing with friends. Hours I could have spent actually at the beach.

I know the rational thing would be to stop and use my time for more important things. And yet, compulsively, I keep on: ripping out and scraping off this natural part of my body, wherever I find it, relishing the sting and the bare flesh left behind.

Rùn-dìomhair; Rùn Dìomhair, Pearsanta?
The Personal Secret

Fearchar

A bheil rud sam bith a bhios nas cunnartaiche na rudeigin a tha air a chumail am falach eadar duine agus a bhean; eadar caraidean; eadar dùthchannan; is mar sin air adhart?

Cha bhi sin furasta. Is tric a bhios daoine ag innse dhomh gum bi mi a' toirt cus fiosrachaidh dhaibh. Cha bhi iadsan a' smaoineachadh gur e duine falchaidh a th' annamsa idir. Ach, leis an fhìrinn innse, 's cinnteach gu bheil rudan dìomhair nam bheatha-sa; agus tha deagh adhbharan ann airson sin. Nach eil stuth aig a h-uile duine nach urrainn dhaibh fhoillseachadh gun a bhith a' cur pian no nàire air daoine eile. Chan urrainn dhomh sin a dhèanamh; ach dè eile a bhios ann?

Nuair a thilg am ministear a-mach à Sgoil-Shàbaide mi a chionn 's gun do dh'fhalaich mi fon bhòrd 's leum mi a-mach air na nigheanan beaga? Chan eil gu leòr ann an sin; 's co-dhiù cha robh mi ach deich bliadhna a dh'aois aig an àm.

Am far-ainm? An dearbh rud. Bu chòir dhomh cnuasachadh air carson a thug sin buaidh cho mòr orm nuair a bha mi òg. Chaidh m' ainmeachadh às dèidh mo dhà sheanair; ach b' ann an-còmhnaidh a bhiodh mo mhàthair ag ràdh gum bu chòir dhan a h-uile duine Rick a chantainn rium. Tha mòran ainmean eile air a bhith air an cur orm bhon uair sin, gun a bhith a' toirt na h-aon bhuaidhe orm agus cha bu chòir dhomh a bhith air dragh a ghabhail nuair a bha daoine a' cleachdadh pàirt den ainm a bha sgrìobhte air mo theisteanas-breith. 'S dòcha gum b' e an comhardadh tuairisgeulach na lùib a bha a' cur cais orm?

Nuair a chunnaic na sgoilearan eile mar a bha mi a' dèiligeadh ris, 's cinnteach gun do thòisich iad ga chleachadh mar sheòrsa de bhurraidheachd. Ann an dòigh, bha sin neònach, a chionn 's gun do sheas mi an aghaidh barrachd air aon bhurraidh, fiù 's far nach b' ann ormsa a bha iad ag obair. Aon turas, sheas mi eadar balach mòr agus balach na bu lugha; ach, b' e rud corporra a bha sin, 's b' ann air m' inntinn a bha am far-ainm agam ag obair.

'S dòcha gum biodh e cuideachail aig an àm seo nam bithinn ag ràdh rudeigin mu mo dheidhinn fhìn. Ged nach biodh e ro dhoirbh dhomh obair-sgoile ionnsachadh agus sgilean-spòrs' a thogail, cha bhithinn cho cofhurtail ann a bhith a' dèanamh chàirdeasan ri daoine is ann a bhith gan cumail.

Chluichinn mòran spòrs agus, ann am buidhnean den t-seòrsa sin, bha mi ceart gu leòr. Cuideachd, fhuair mi cuid de chuiridhean a dhol gu àiteachan còmhla ri balaich eile; ach, b' ann glè ainneamh a bhithinn-sa faisg air an teis-mheadhan de bhuidheann sam bith. Cha b' ann dhòmhsa a b' urrainn caraid sam bith a chumail dlùth orm fad ùine mhòir agus bu mhise a-mhàin a bu choireach ris a' sin.

Ged a bha mi uaigneach nam nàdar, cha b' ann tric a bhithinn aonaranach; ach, nuair a bhithinn ann am buidheann, uaireannan bhithinn a' faireachdainn cianail iomallach. Bhiodh eagal orm nach biodh daoine eile a' gabhail rium no gum biodh iad a' magadh orm. Airson an adhbhar sin, 's dòcha nach robh e na iongnadh gum bu mhise targaid na burraidheachd den t-seòrsa seo?

Bu toigh leum cuimhne a bhith agam air mar a thòisich i – tha e neònach gur ann boireann a tha am facal 'burraidheachd'! – ach chan ann agamsa. Ach, às dèidh greise, nam bithinn anns an raon-chluiche leam fhìn, bhiodh feadhainn ag èigheach an fhar-ainme agam agus bu tric a bhiodh iad na b' òige na bha mise. 'S dòcha gun cuir e iongnadh oirbh, ach b' ann glè ainneamh a bhiodh clann mòran na bu shine na mìse a' cur dragh orm idir.

Carson a bhiodh iad ga dhèanamh? Tha dùil agam gum b' e rud spòrsail a bh' ann dhaibhsan ach bhiodh ùidh na bu mhotha agamsa ann a bhith a' faighinn a-mach cò às a thàinig am far-ainm agus dè a bha air a chùlaibh.

Bhiodh e fìor a ràdh gu bheil a' chiad phàirt ceart, gu litireil co-dhiu; ach tha mi cinnteach nach ann bhon a' sin a thàinig e. Is ciall eile dha agus tha dùil agam gum b' e sin an tùs na bu chreideasaiche. Ach carson a bhiodh iad a' cur sin ormsa? A chionn 's gum bite a' dèanamh comhardadh; no mar thoradh air rudeigin a rinn mise? Chan eil càil a dh'fhios a'm!

Ann an aon dòigh, chan e rud cudromach a bh' ann; ach, còrr is leth-cheud bliadhna on a dh'fhag mi an sgoil, tha e fhathast ag obair air m' inntinn. Cha bhi am far-ainm fhèin a' cur dragh sam bith orm san latha an-diugh, ach is tric a bhios mi a' smaoineachadh air fhathast. Carson?

An-dè, leugh mi pìos le Mata Todd mu dheidhinn a' chroin a bhithear a' dèanamh le burraidheachd thòcail, gu h-àraidh air co-sheòrsaich òga. Cho dona 's cho maireannach a b' urrainn dha a bhith; agus rinn sin ciall dhòmhsa. 'S dòcha gur e sin as coireach, gu ìre, gu bheil misneachd a dhìth orm, a chionn 's nach b' urrainn dhomh a-riamh a bhith cinnteach mu dè cho math 's a bhithinn air rud sam bith a dhèanamh no mu na beachdan a bhiodh aig daoine eile mu mo dheidhinn, ged nach b' ann ri co-sheòrsachd a bha an gnothach a' buntainn.

'S cinnteach, co-dhiù, gum biodh mo bheatha gu tur eadar-dhealaichte gun ghuth air 'Big Head Fred'!

* * *

A secret, a personal secret?

Is there anything more dangerous than things kept hidden between men and women, friends, countries, etc?

That won't be easy. As usual people say to me I'm too free with my information. They don't think I'm at all a secretive person. But to tell the truth it's certain there are secrets in my life, and there are good reasons for that. Doesn't everyone have stuff they cannot disclose without causing pain or shame to other people? I can't do that, but what else is there?

When the minister threw me out of Sunday school because I hid under the table and jumped out at the young girls? There's not enough in that and anyway I was only ten at the time.

The nickname? The very thing. I ought to reflect on why that had such an impact on me when I was young. I was named after my two grandfathers but my mother always said that people should call me Rick. I've been called many names since without the same impact and people using part of the name on my birth certificate should not have worried me. Perhaps it was the rhyming description in it that wound me up?

It's certain that when other pupils saw my reaction to it they started to use it as a sort of bullying. In a way that was strange because I stood up to more than one bully, even when it wasn't me they were bullying. I went between a big boy and a smaller boy, but that was physical, and the nickname worked on my mind.

Perhaps it would be helpful at this point if I told you something about myself. Although it wasn't too difficult for me to learn schoolwork and sports skills, I wasn't so comfortable making and keeping friends. I played many sports and in groups like that I was alright. I also got some invites to go places with other boys, but I was seldom at the centre of any group. I couldn't keep any close friend for long, and it was entirely my own fault.

Although I was solitary I wasn't often lonely, but when I was in a group I would sometimes feel terribly isolated. I would be scared that the others didn't want me or that they were mocking me. For that reason, perhaps it wasn't surprising that I would be the target of this type of bullying.

I would like to remember how it started but I can't. But after a while, if I was in the playground myself, there would be a few shouting the nickname at me. Often they were younger than myself. It might surprise you but rarely did kids much older than me bother me at all.

Why did they do it? I expect it was fun for them, but I would be more interested in where the nickname came from and what was behind it.

It would be fair to say that the first part was anatomically correct, but I'm sure that's not where it came from. There is another meaning to it, and I expect that that provides a more credible answer. But why did they use it in my case. Because it created a rhyme or because of something I did? I haven't a clue!

In one way, there's nothing to it; but, more than fifty years since leaving school, it is still working on my mind. The nickname itself doesn't worry me today, but I still think of it frequently. Why?

I read a piece by Matthew Todd yesterday about the damage done by emotional bullying, especially to young, gay people. How bad and how lasting it could be, and it made sense to me. Perhaps that's part of the reason I lack confidence. Because I could never be sure of how good I was at anything, nor of the opinion of others about me, although it wasn't about homosexuality.

Anyway, it's certain my life would be completely different without 'Big Head Fred'!

A Gift of Knowing

Stephen Frame

I saw a naked woman when I was maybe eight or nine. Her nakedness was given, not taken by accident or with furtive intent, as it so often is.

I already knew what a fanny looked like (men's bits had a whole lexicography all to themselves but, back then, women had fannies and there it ended). Now and again, one of our gang would find a scud book, usually up the old railway that ran past the field we played in. It would be spread out on the grass, hunkered over and flicked through, shared. Until somebody would start to laugh, maybe a strained laugh, and grab at the pages. So somebody else would grab back. Then we all would and the scud book would be torn and scattered, its power broken, as we sent tits and bums aloft in the breeze.

That was the way of it, in our secret world away from the adults. It was the early '70s and our world was 'away ootside and play', so our world was the street and the swing park and the coo's park.

I was in the cadre of little brothers that hung around with our big brothers, who all hung around together. Our big brothers were worldly-wise Olympians of eleven and twelve, who could outrun, outfight and out football us minnows. Any day, right? So their opinion on matters was gospel.

Like the fact that one of the older brothers, Jim, had an older sister, June. Who was a ride, as we used to say (crude but it got to the heart of things without wasting too many words). June had long black hair. June was a teenager. What a ride might involve was a hazy concept, but the older brothers held it in high regard, so it was treated with due gravity by all.

I don't remember exactly how it started, I just remember what happened after it started. And it was so far off the chart, so far off the radar of my eight- or nine-year-old experience...

We were always doing stuff, mostly kids' stuff, but once in a while, our imaginations would lead us into darker territory. 'It's deid. Tie some fishin' gut roon its leg. Fling it ower the phone wire. When a caur comes, pul it up in front i' the winscreen.' What else would you do with a hedgehog's corpse?

It must have been Jim who told us his sister was in the shower. He was the betrayer, but we were all the conspirators. We would sneak into his house for a look.

We piled through the front door, into the hallway. Which arrowed straight to the bathroom at the end. Where the door was a bit open. We could see the shower curtain pulled across the length of the bath. We could hear the shower running. Somewhere behind it was June. With nothing on. Naked. In the scud.

As a squirming scrum of bodies, we edged forward, pushed back, eagerness warring with trepidation. June heard us. It would have been impossible not to. Her head appeared from behind the curtain, hair draped in wet strings. She didn't say a word. She didn't have to. We broke and ran.

Only, not me. I was small, I got pushed to the front and I didn't know what to do, caught in that hallway. Frozen. Alone. June looked at me for the longest time, not angry or upset. Thoughtful maybe, considering. Then she said, 'Would you like to see?' So far off the chart, so far off the radar. Way, way, way beyond answering. She stepped out of the shower. She stood.

She let me look. She silently disappeared back behind the curtain.

I didn't run out of the house screaming, 'Ah've seen June's fanny!' I didn't tell the gang. I didn't tell anyone. Why not? This was like scoring the winning penalty in a Scotland v England match. Well, mibbe no that good.

I remember I wasn't excited; it was a calm moment. I looked with wonder, at something you're not supposed to see, that you're not yet ready to see but are suddenly presented with. Something secret. Something important. Not with guilt or shame. With honesty.

Maybe. Maybe the years have put a patina of meaning on it that never existed. But something passed between us that day, I'm sure. A gift given. A gift of knowing, in water-sheened flesh.

I Haven't Been Breathing Lately

Aynsleigh Hollywood

Did I have to tell everyone
in one day
Did I have to pour my heart out
to them all
I had only just accepted
that I haven't been breathing lately
I will say that I got drunk
It happens, so what
Get yourself into a state that is unsafe
and your mother will worry too
So I told her that now I am
out of education which has been twenty years of my life
I can't see the road ahead
and it has been making breathing hard
Twenty years of my life is over
and so much is in front of me that I can't see
It started two months ago when my subconscious asked me
Will you ever be happy
I didn't have an answer for once in my life
and that made my chest tight
and my breathing laboured
I ignored it, knowing it would go away
but it ebbed and flowed for those two months
until I drank to make it shut up
I told my mum as I reaped the consequences
and I told my boss as she yelled at me down the phone
for calling in with self-imposed illness

Two months living with a chest of varying levels of
    tightness
that time spent living with stress and being silent
Thinking, it will go away, it is just a phase
I told my colleagues, I told my friends,
I told my parents, I told my brother
They hugged me
and with each hug, squeezing me so tight
I felt the breath come back
I confess, I have not been breathing lately
and now that I have let that out
Maybe I can learn to breathe again.

Secrets of a Dog Lover

Gail A Brown

I like my dog more than I like many humans.
A statement not meant to offend man or woman,
But he is my friend, my companion, my boy,
All he asks for are walks, a warm bed and a toy.

My dog's shown me nature, secret places to go,
A love for the land perhaps not there before,
Sunrises, sunsets; some days bleary-eyed ventures,
Filling lungs with fresh air and the scent of adventure.

He welcomes me home with a dance and a wiggle,
Slapping his tail on his body and making me giggle,
Bringing shoe, sock, hat, glove as my welcoming platter,
An outpouring of love so I know that I matter.

I haven't seen humans do the welcome-home dance,
Instead leaving the truths of delight down to chance,
What if we tried it, what joy would be in it,
If we danced for the loved ones just gone for a minute.

I don't mean my dog's perfect, he's not even quite good,
He barks on his lead and can sometimes be rude,
He is nervous and jumpy, hates traffic, surprises,
For him no Facebook filter; for his faults no disguises.

When he lies on my lap all these faults are forgiven,
I'm reminded that I am his reason for living,
He tells me his stories without saying a word,
A dog's talked to you too, but you may not have heard.

My dog loves me whatever, on both good days and bad,
Whether happy or grumpy, whether selfish or sad,
A grey hair, a wrinkle, a smile telling lies,
Through it all my dog looks with the same loving eyes.

My dog has sharp teeth but won't use them to bite me,
He has strong limbs, and claws, but won't use them to
    fight me,
When I loosen his lead he could go, run away,
But he always comes back; choosing only to stay.

With him I find solitude without being alone,
A warm beating heart binding family; home,
No grudges are held, and all humans are equal,
No need for possessions – he'll leave those to people.

A dog stays by your side till his very last day,
And he'll walk to the ends of the earth if you say,
When a dog dies he leaves us awash with emotion,
For a life filled with love and the sweetest devotion.

So these are my reasons, for the secret I've told you,
Dogs might make better humans, but I'm not here to
    scold you,
Let's just listen and learn from these friends we hold close,
Because sometimes the ones who say nothing know most.

And if dogs became humans, wouldn't that be exciting,
A world with less judgement, less hate and less fighting.
So that's my confession, not too shocking but true,
And if humans were dogs I'd like them the best too.

General Lending

Gill Monaghan

It's May 1992 and I'm currently on placement at Dundee Central Library. My days consist of putting returned books back on the shelves, filing, reorganising, assisting with enquiries and serving customers at the counter. To an avid young reader and fantasist like me, I feel like I've won the work-experience lottery. My local library in Menzieshill is fascinating enough – I mean, I found *The Hitchhiker's Guide to the Galaxy* on the first shelf I looked – but it's small. The Central Library is HUGE, with row upon row of pine shelving and white, wire carousels of knowledge. It even has a separate Children's Library *and* audio/visual borrowing room!

The old man arrives seemingly out of nowhere. He is small and crumpled with a stoop. He stops to blow his nose with an old, tatty, brown-and-cream handkerchief before slowly making his way towards the counter.

'Can I help you, sir?'

'Jist returning these, lassie,' he says, handing over a carrier bag full of books.

'Certainly,' I say, beginning to scan the barcodes. All of a sudden, a message flashes up on the computer monitor. OVERDUE. Amount £6.

'Sir, it says that your books are overdue and that you have a fee to pay. Six pounds.'

I look into his wearied face and I see the bottom of his world fall out. He tells me that he hasn't been keeping particularly well since the passing of his wife some months before, that the days run into each other and that he forgets things a lot more. Momentarily, I'm caught off guard. What should I do? Speak to the librarian? What would be the *decent* thing?

'Sir,' I say, checking that the coast is clear, 'consider the fee waived.'

He argues with me a little, out of pride, but with the click of a button, his debt is no more. He thanks me and I feel good that he can put that £6 to some other use. That's my good deed done for the day ... or is it?

Another lady who arrives at the counter with a tremor, who can barely pass the books over the counter, never mind be expected to count out coins of change is met with a cheery, 'Library-fee amnesty today!' Then there's the harassed young mother who looks so relieved that I feel like she's going to jump over the counter and hug me when I say with a grin, 'Don't worry about the fine.'

I decide that the more affluent customers (and there are plenty of them) can handle £1.50 here and there, but my fellow skint comrades are absolved of their fiscal hardship. From that moment onwards, I'm like the latter-day Robina Hood of lending, an intellectual freedom fighter, a one-girl literary hardship fund, writing off the debts of the elderly and disadvantaged with a wink and whisper of, 'It's okay. We've all been there.'

'Oh, hiya, Mrs Wilson. How are you today? How is your wee dog doing? Okay, there's a fine on that book, but I won't say anything if you won't.' Click. Mrs Wilson looks delighted and smiles through her spectacles at me as we proceed to have a wander around the library together, chatting (very quietly – we don't forget where we are) about Vince, her West Highland terrier who we wave to through the glass of the window.

After my week is done, I reckon I've cleared the reading debt of just about a tenth of Dundee's population and am on first-name terms with a great number of the elderly patrons. Then the head librarian calls me into the back office… to thank me for all of my hard work, and I receive a glowing report to take back to school with me '… a pleasant attitude to both staff and customers… picked up library procedures easily… Gillian worked well without supervision.' Indeed.

Dundee Central Library, I'm writing to apologise for not following the rules of my placement and contributing to libraries' funding problems. But you see, the thing is, I couldn't find it in my fourteen-year-old self to charge the elderly and underprivileged natives of my city for still being curious about life, for wishing to remain well read and for being so charming and friendly to my slightly naïve younger self. To a penniless, working-class teenager, the contents of those shelves were my window into other worlds and escape route from this one, and I guess that's what made me do it. I don't wish to sound like I didn't value the experience you gave me. I worked with a wonderful bunch of friendly, warm, highly knowledgeable and funny people at the library who I learned so much from and who were such a positive influence on me. Our libraries are great institutions with dedicated staff that deserve to be cherished… but so do the loyal people who patronise them, as disorganised, as forgetful, as heartbroken and hard up as they sometimes can be.

Franchise

Kirsty Lear-Grant

I must confess that I thought Santa ran some sort of franchise when I was six. Not only did he manage Christmas from the 735 pages of the Kays catalogue, but he also ran the Christmas hamper scheme. Santa, being a busy man and all, sometimes needs a wee heads-up. So, when Mum told us that our Christmas hamper came from Santa via one of his many helpers, a perfect opportunity was presented to me. I remember the hamper arriving that very Christmas.

Mum is upstairs having a lie down 'cause her back is still sore from putting the tree up last week. Me and Jimmy – that's my wee brother – are sitting on the wee couch and I have the Kays catalogue on my knee. It slides off my legs sometimes 'cause I'm wearing slippy yellow tights. I turn the pages right to the back where all the good stuff is, like the toys. I'm in charge of the catalogue 'cause I'm the biggest. Jimmy helps me look but he's too wee to touch. The catalogue smells like nail varnish and it is shiny and full of hundreds and millions of pages; that's why it's so huge. Santa's elves must work really hard to make all this stuff. I lick my finger and touch the top of the page. It sticks like glue and I can turn it over easily. It makes Jimmy laugh 'cause he thinks I'm magic. Somebody is knocking at the front door and I don't know what to do. I know that we're not to answer the door in case it's Joe the Provie man looking for money, and I'm too wee to say that Mum's not in. I shut the catalogue and slide it onto the couch.

'Mum, Mummy, Mum, door,' Jimmy is shouting.

'Shhhhhhh.' I put my finger to my lips. 'Hide behind the couch.'

Jimmy is a good boy and goes behind the couch 'cause that's what we always do, but I can see him peeping. *Lassie* is on the telly and there isnae any sound on, but I'm scared in case it is Joe 'cause he sometimes looks in the window. I turn off the big button and hide. Mum doesn't like Joe, but I do 'cause he's smiley and funny like my dad. He has white hair but he isn't old like Papa. He always wears a shiny red tie and a pen clipped onto his shirt pocket. It's good fun though, crouching down on the carpet with our hands over our mouths, trying not to laugh. Mum usually crouches down beside us so that she can shush us, but it makes us laugh like anything. Anyway, Mum is too big to be invisible.

Inside the house everything is as quiet as anything, but I can still hear the knock, knock, knock, and I can hear the ceiling creaking, so Mum must have got up.

'Answer the door, Kirsten; it's one of Santa's helpers.'

I'm off the floor and bombing it to the door before the knocking stops. I stand on the bottom stair and turn the handle. There's a wee fat man with puffy red cheeks wearing a Santa hat.

'Parcel for Mrs Clark.' He's holding a ma-hoosive brown box and looking behind me for something.

'I'm coming, I'm coming.' Mum's in her pink nighty even though it's still daytime. There's a fag in her mouth with a long bendy bit of ash on it; it's ready to fall off on the stair. She's puffing and huffing and clinging to the bannister while she wobbles down towards us.

'You couldnae take it in, son? My back is killing me.'

'No problem.'

Santa's elf is in our house! I hope he likes the decorations. I pop my head outside and check for Joe's white van, but it's not there so I shut the door. In the living room, Mum writes her name on a wee notebook that's magic 'cause of the blue paper that's underneath it – it makes her name write twice.

'Nice tree,' he says and pats Jimmy on the head and then squeezes my cheek. 'Merry Christmas. I hope Santa's good to you.'

The elf walks to the front door and my belly is all funny because of the hamper, but also 'cause I have ripped a picture out of page 631 of the catalogue without Mum noticing. I follow him out to the big hedge and tug on his jumper sleeve.

'Can you please give this to Santa, just in case?'

He opens the folded piece of shiny paper and smiles.

'Sure thing, hen. Mind and be a good girl then.'

I watch him get into his car. He's looking at the picture of the Patosa doll that I picked especially, and he's laughing. It must be because I sneaked it to him.

After the Dark Night Comes the Morning

Emma J Myatt

My confession is this: that I nearly let the darkness win.

Nobody knows how dark it was. On the outside I've always been happy-go-lucky, the life and soul, room-brightening, smiling Emma. The party girl. Someone with loads of energy. Inside, it's been a different story. And this is my secret.

It came in many forms: anger, self-hatred, self-harm, self-doubt, destructive behaviour; a total lack of self-esteem.

In my fortieth year I finally understood what it was: depression, an illness that had affected me for over half my life. I knew I had blue days and weeks – darkness would suddenly descend for no reason and cripple me. Usually I hid from the world because when I was down, I couldn't explain it to anyone. The fear and insomnia and rage made life a constant challenge, with a lot of stress. I never stopped pushing myself, to meet people, take on challenges, travel, explore, experience, but inside I was terrified; of people not liking me, of failing, of letting anyone close. I'd meet a new boyfriend and suddenly I'd be teetering on a precipice. I used to have to lock myself in the loo and hug myself and cry and force myself to go back to him, face the thought that I might be rejected. The same happened with friends: at first everything was okay until the friendship moved up a notch and I'd become convinced that they didn't like me. I'd have a conversation; then later analyse every word, looking for ways I'd screwed up.

I was desperate to get rid of this endlessly critical inner voice. I was desperate not to get so angry at those closest to me. My anger came out regularly and ruined everything. After I'd got angry I'd retreat somewhere and punch myself, hard, in the face, the arms, the legs. I bruised myself to punish myself for hurting other people.

I moved around a lot. I made friends, had lovers, but there was this constant fear that they would see the 'real me' and run a mile. I moved to Malaysia to try and sort myself out and get away from certain things. In Malaysia I drank a lot.

I continued to fight the darkness but it got harder; the blue periods got longer and it was harder to pull myself out of them. I kept telling myself I could beat it. I still lived fully and had fun in extreme surges of energy; when I look back I see times I was happy. I still hid in the blue times. The underlying stress of hating myself was *always* there, sapping my strength.

Into this mess walked Hamish, when I was 27. Hamish, a Scottish rock, withstood all the storms – and there were plenty. We left Malaysia and rode 50,000 miles back to Scotland on a motorbike called Bertha. I spent around 1,500 hours in my own head, on the back of the bike. The same things came to mind over and over: the anger, the regrets. The darkness was still there, even on this trip of a lifetime – with no routine it was harder to keep it at bay. I made a decision to get proper therapy, because I was stuck and sad and scared and I'd had enough. I was exhausted.

We moved to Scotland and I saw a therapist. She helped me, and for the first time, I discovered how to like myself.

Hame and I had two children in quick succession. It was amazing – and terrifying. I loved them so much but was convinced I was a terrible mother. The darkness got worse, post-birth. I became quite ill and was eventually diagnosed with Graves' disease, an autoimmune condition that affects the thyroid and therefore the whole body. This was – and still is – treated with medication. I fought against the darkness, but it got harder and harder. I was convinced the children would be better off without me. Some days I wanted to push the double buggy to the harbour, leave it in a safe place and jump in. Other days, alone in the car on the way to pick them up from nursery, my hands twitched – what if I swerved, just a little, into the path of that oncoming lorry?

In the end I knew I *had* to try and get help. I owed it to my young family, to Hamish – and to myself. I went to my GP, who listened and asked lots of questions, one of which was: what do you see happening in the future? After a pause, I realised I could see no future. At all. He prescribed antidepressants, and I began to get better. I started sleeping properly for the first time in over twenty years. Physical symptoms I'd never realised were part of depression disappeared. The anger became manageable.

I'm still on medication. I'm convinced that untreated depression contributed to my developing Graves'. I'm convinced that my total lack of self-esteem contributed to the depression. We've helped our children (now six and seven) develop as much self-esteem as we can. I've been, and am, a good mother. Even in the dark years.

In April this year, I was hanging out the washing with my children, cats and chickens around my feet. I felt completely contented. And then a feeling: something was coming.

A few days later I found a lump in my breast and on Friday 13 May I was diagnosed with breast cancer. I've lost the last few weeks somewhere, but I'm still laughing.

Yesterday, my lovely mum arrived to help look after me.

The darkness hasn't beaten me. Today, I'm happier than I've ever been. I live more fully, love completely and don't waste a single minute of precious life. I am now, aged forty-three, that strong positive person that everyone else – except me – could see.

I will beat this. It's one more battle against the darkness that whispers: how much do you *really* want to live?

The answer is – very much.

The Confession

Jo Clifford

I didn't know how to tell her.

I'd never told anyone I was terrified. But I knew I had to.

I loved her so deeply, and I was beginning to realise she loved me too; and I was so afraid that after I told her she wouldn't love me anymore.

That she'd be as disgusted with me as I was with myself. And I wasn't sure I could bear that.

For there'd been a long time when I really believed that if anyone came to know this about me I would die of shame.

But I had to do it.

So that night I said…

I can't remember what I said. I can't remember how I put it, but the thing was…

We hadn't been going out very long, less than a week, but we'd known each other for months.

I know there is such a thing as love at first sight, because that's how it was the first time I saw her. She was staying in our flat until term began. She was sitting with her feet up on our sofa. She was wearing the most beautiful long black silk antique skirt. She was in pain. She had cystitis.

Not very romantic, I suppose, but I didn't mind and went round and knocked up one of my lecturers who lived nearby to ask if they had any bicarbonate of soda.

And they did, and it helped, and then for weeks afterwards whenever she came round to see us I would hold my breath, hoping she would come up the stairs to my room in the attic.

And I felt so happy when she did...

And then eventually we had a drink together in a grotty pub called the Whey Pat, and we seemed to understand each other so well.

But I was very scared of telling her, and I learnt later she was very scared of telling me, until one night there was a party in the cottage she lived in and I got a bit drunk and kissed her.

And I thought she would be so furious with me but she wasn't – she looked ecstatically happy.

And that's how we ended up in bed together.

It was so lovely. But I couldn't get a hard-on.

It wasn't because I didn't think she was sexy – I did. I thought she was the most beautiful person I had ever met. It was just...

And there was something else too. Something else I couldn't tell her.

I couldn't tell her I'd fallen for her the minute I saw her photo, maybe six months before, because that would have been most utterly ridiculous.

I was studying in Granada at the time, and my best friend had sent me the student newspaper with her photo on the front page. I'd thought she was so beautiful and that she was the kind of person I would love to have a relationship with. Only that was ridiculous.

Because she was fashionable and glamorous and had lived in San Francisco and was going to be the editor of the student newspaper. Whereas I...

I was lonely and unfashionable and ugly and most painfully shy.

And I was spending my time going to the Alhambra, mostly, and writing stories and poems and possessed with this stupid dream of becoming a writer.

I would eat alone, mostly, and there were two shops

I would go past on the way to the cheap restaurant where I ate.

One had the most gorgeous women's underwear and the other one lovely flamenco dresses, and I so wanted to be able to wear both.

I was far too frightened and ashamed to look openly into the windows and would kind of sidle past them, looking at them sideways, because I couldn't bear the thought of anyone seeing me looking in.

And various men had propositioned me, which I couldn't really deal with at all because, before she died, my mum had instilled in me a real terror of men having sex with me – and anyway, as far as I could tell, that wasn't what I wanted at all.

What turned me on was the thought of being a woman and wearing women's clothes, and that wasn't the same thing at all. That was a wicked and disgusting thing, I thought, and tried very hard not to think it.

But what it also meant was that I didn't really want to have sex with women either, and I'd just broken up with a really lovely girl called Barbara because I was far too ashamed to talk about it all.

But with Susie it was different. I had to talk to her. And I said...

Well I couldn't tell her all that, and I couldn't tell her the truth either, which was that in trying to repress my being trans, I had repressed my own sexuality. And a whole load of other things besides...

But I couldn't tell her that because 'trans' wasn't even a word at the time. There was no word I knew for the way I was. It was just unspeakable.

So I can't remember what I said. I must have stammered something about wanting to be a girl and being ashamed of it and she said...

She said…

She said she'd always known there was something very feminine about me and that was one reason why she liked me.

And her saying that saved my life.

And we did learn to make love to each other, and it was wonderful, and we had two daughters and they made us very happy.

They're both grown up now, and so very gifted and talented and successful and loving and beautiful. And I have a grandson too…

I loved Susie for thirty-three years, and she loved me. From the time we first met until the time she died. And I love her still.

The January Fashion Confession

Billy Letford

The hat
My aunt shops online using Glen's
vodka and Irn-Bru to channel the Christmas
spirit. Last year she downloaded some
knitting patterns, began a self-prescribed
course of codeine, then went to work on gifts
for the family. I received the yellow and
red Mohawk hat with ear flaps and tassels.
Something magic had happened in the knit.
Somewhere in the opiate induced
alcohol and Irn-Bru trance my aunt
had found the shamanic. A melted quality
more like a Mohawk flame than a hat.

The coat
Is a twenty-year-old hand-me-down parka
my uncle wore in the nineties when
he thought he was Liam Gallagher. Some of
the swagger was left in it. I find the rolling
motion helps to lift and plant the feet.

The boots
Are surplus Dutch army bought during the
Forest of Ae World Ceilidh to help combat
the difficult suck of the festival quagmire.
I've discovered they're just as suited
to an icy pavement on a tricky Tuesday.

The canter
Is how you'll find me, a yellow and red
flame above a nineties parka and a pair of
Dutch army boots, sure of foot and swift
of thought with a swagger to match,
cutting through the frost like a blow torch.